The Soul of Caregiving

A Caregiver's Guide to
Healing and Transformation

by Edward M. Smink, Ph.D.

Just as the pomegranate reveals its inner secrets in due season,

so too, does Soul refresh with insight and wisdom.

Synopsis

Who are the caregivers? We all are, for at the heart of being human is the capacity to care, to reach out to others and explore the relationships we build. *The Soul of Caregiving* is about us and how we, as caregivers, serve, even sacrifice, for those in need. I invite you to explore with me how we have the opportunities to partake in a kind of pilgrimage along the path of our experiences as caregivers. Who will be your guide on this journey? Unlike other pilgrims who have a guide assigned to them, you will soon discover it is your own Soul guiding you. Professionally skilled as we may be to meet the needs of others, a fundamental core component of our busy lives as caregivers, is the necessity to stop and rest. It is not a waste of time, but rather a luxury of time, to ponder, reflect, and grow from our experiences. Not an easy endeavor in the midst of a whirlwind of activity. We, as caregivers, experience vulnerability, helplessness, fears, and pain over the traumatic events we experience because we care. We care about those whom we are called to serve. Compassion fatigue comes about because we care.

In Chapter One, I call this tension between activity and reflection, "the Dance of Caregiving," a dance between the caregiver's needs and those of the one in need. The chapter is an introduction to exploring something we do every day: to reflect on our experiences. Chapter Two, "Reclaiming Soul," asks the question, "What is Soul?" and how is the caregiver empowered and sustained. Discovering Soul implies going deeper into the inner caverns of our being and listening to the inner beats of our heart where insight and wisdom abide. "Once Upon a Time in the Land of OZ," Chapter Three, explores the universal underpinnings of the role of caregiving, as each profession exists in the broader mythic and archetypal realm of a culture.

In Chapter Four, "Truce or Consequences," both the mythos and logos of caregiving are explored. Each relates to faithless science and unscientific faith, leading to a unity of the left and right brain functions. The Ins and Outs of Hospitality," in Chapter Five, discusses how the caregiver, as host, experiences three different dimensions of hospitality: the caregiver who hosts the stranger, the caregiver who welcomes the stories of the guests they host, and thirdly, the caregiver who hosts his or her reactions and experiences. Chapter Six, "Love is a Wounded Healer," addresses an ancient question of the frailty of humankind. There is within each of us a space that seeks wholeness and transformation, an area of woundedness which often shows its face in the midst of our caregiving. In a unique and profound way, those who serve are transformed in the healing relationship that is created with those in need. We are wounded healers.

"Cultivating the Soul's Garden," Chapter Seven, addresses the art of reflection as a fundamental skill for caregivers. An understanding of Soul implies allowing the moment to take root and to reflect on how to nourish and sustain ourselves as caregivers. Chapter Eight focuses on "Spirituality: The Sinew of Human Experience" where imagination helps one discover meaning, arguing that the essential actions of a caregiver are spiritual. In Chapter Nine "Practice, Practice, Practice" I explore what a practice is and how caregiving is a spiritual practice. The ordinary becomes spiritual, as inner strengths and values give birth to meaning, insight, and transformation. The *"Soul of Caregiving"* concludes with Chapter Ten, "Warning: Our Tank is Almost Empty" which explores compassion fatigue and its two sisters, secondary traumatic stress and burnout. We experience compassion fatigue because we care. We look at how to recognize the warning signs, take action to avoid them, and learn how to recover from them in building compassion resilience.

Each chapter invites the reader to ponder and reflect. There are questions at the end of each chapter to facilitate this process.

Reviews

As a "caregiver" several times over (Nurse by training; primary caregiver for 86-year-old mom suffering from dementia; spouse of someone with a life-threatening illness, leadership coach), it was easy for me to read Ed's stories and see myself within them. His prose, stories, quotes, and references to esteemed authors provides validation for our common humanity. Ed's integration of humor helped me to notice my own shadows, and embrace them with compassion, and light. Perhaps most importantly, Ed helped to bring into the light the common syndrome of "compassion fatigue" where we, as caregivers, may come face-to-face with our darkest shadow where we find anger, hostility, sarcasm, and aggression Ed normalizes these reactions and aptly reminds us to practice forgiveness. His courageous, personal illustrations where he showcases his own vulnerability remind us that we are in conversation with someone who's "been there; done that." *The Soul of Caregiving* is not a book to be rushed through. It is a non-judging companion that one could pick up during many phases of our life.

– Joy W. Goldman RN, MS, PCC Certified Physician Development Coach Leadership/Executive Coach

Although I don't see myself as a caregiver, I know I have been in situations where I have given care to others. Reading this book has allowed me to pause and own the caregiving I have given to others. I can honestly tell you that I was pleasantly "sucked in" to the book. In the beginning, I was captured by Ed's reference to "Soul Pain". I believe we all can relate to some inner pain, but often times we don't know what it is, so it is almost impossible to identify it and put a name on it. I was quickly drawn in with the gentle tone of the book, the metaphors, and the humor. I thoroughly enjoyed hearing Ed's personal experiences and being able to see his personality in his writing as I know him as a coaching colleague.

– Valarie Hayes, Certified Leadership Coach, Career Advisor.

Edward shares extensively from his wealth of life experience. This is a fascinating book on the profound differences between caretaking and caregiving. I highly recommend this book for the lifelong learner. Be prepared to do some soul searching.

– Barbara S. Hennessy, MS,
Certified Rehabilitation Counselor (CRC)

Dr. Smink has written the ultimate guide for caregivers. ***The Soul of the Caregiver - A Caregivers Guide to Healing and Transformation*** is a work of art from the very first page to the last. For those who dare to take an intimate journey within oneself and look deep down inside of one's own soul and connect with their Higher Power as they never have before. This work of art will take you there. We cannot give what we ourselves have not yet discovered, Dr. Smink's book helps you discover that it is not what happens to us that is important, but what we DO with what has happened... that's the "transformation" we have all been looking for.

– Richard Hirbe, fsp, Masters of Pastoral Counseling, Board Certified
Chaplain

The Soul of Caregiving has something for everyone, stories, academic research, enhanced definitions, an honest look at caregiving and one's role in it...and the sentence that says it all, "There is nothing objective about spirituality."

– Jean M. Lambert, SVP, Mission Integration, Catholic Health
Initiatives, (retired)

Caregiving requires an openness to one's own vulnerability, as one is with another. Facing, understanding, and embracing one's own brokenness is not a necessary hurdle to overcome for being an effective caregiver, but it is the very soul of heroic caregiving. Dr. Smink takes us on an incredible rich and nuanced journey through the ages, evoking the sages of myths, symbols, psychology and spirituality to lead the reader along the redemptive mystery of caregiving and the inevitable call to self-truth and love at the heart of being not an effective but heroic caregiver. His "Timeout: A Moment of Reprieve - Time for a stop on the journey" at the end of each chapter provided ideal moments for honest self-appraisal and compassion. Thank you, Edward!

– David Lichter, D. Min. Executive Director,
National Association of Catholic Chaplains

I was overwhelming expecting this book to be so "scholarly" that I would not be able to find myself in it. But instead, I found a gracefully flowing use of a body of work which moved perfectly from the Introduction to Chapter 10. What I discovered was a work that incorporates research in different cultures, religions, philosophies, medicine, psychology and other fascinating insights. The stories were phenomenal. I can see where readers can find themselves in some situation and can find benefit in the particular story. I found that each tale has a kernel or two of "therapy" or advice in it that can be useful in addition to the recognition and resemblance factors that readers will discover.

– Pearl Mohnkern, Regional VP of Human Recourses, CHRISTUS
Health and Kentucky One Health HR Market Leader (retired)

The Soul of Caregiving is a most meaningful work not only for those who are caregivers in the healthcare industry but for all those who willingly give themselves in many caregiving ways to make others feel better. The work is pleasantly and surprisingly engaging leading me and I hope other readers to pause and reflect on our special calling as a caregiver, of the sacred and transformative work that we do, and how we can build compassion resilience with self-care.

– Dr Tom Royer, MD. CEO and Partner,
Royer-Maddox-Herron Advisors

This is an excellent work. While I found parts of The Soul of Caregiving difficult to read and reflect on, Eds work has given me the opportunity to really think about my journey. I, as you know, do a much better job caring for others than myself. This is an area I continue to focus on. I try to share my learning with others in my life and those I work with. I think this will be a good read for everyone in a caring profession especially those who are ready to take time to reflect. What a different journey we all would have had had we reflected early on.

– Carol Schmekel BSN, MHSA, Schmekel Consulting

I was surprised to discover that my perspective about caregiving was broadened and enriched by Edward's work *The Soul of Caregiving*. This book takes its readers on a deeply reflective journey, and as such needs to be read slowly or as Edward has quoted "bit by bit." His sense of humor around a lot of the subject matter, added a lightheartedness and entry or permission to explore one's personal and professional life as a caregiver.

– Winifred Stump, BSN, RN, MS, CPPS, CHSP, System Director,
Safety Programs, Catholic Health Initiatives
Enterprise Risk Management Group

I really like the examples and illustrations. Throughout the book, the personal stories are so touching. These are a key element of the "story" Edward is telling and really illustrates the principles he is addressing in a practical way. The chapter on woundedness is profound. Certainly, this chapter can touch everyone. Whether the reader intends to or not, the theme of reflection engages the reader, touches on the danger and vulnerability of being involved as well as the opportunity for healing.

– John L. Zipprich II, General Counsel and Senior Vice President of
International Collaborations for CHRISTUS Health (retired) and
present board member of the SCH Healthcare System

The Soul of Caregiving: A Caregiver's Guide to Healing and Transformation

Copyright © 2018 Edward M. Smink
www.SoulofCaregiving.com

Project Managed with AuthorDock.com
Interior Layout by Brian Schwartz
Cover Design by Tatiana Fernandez
Photo Credit: Nixson Borah

ATTENTION CORPORATIONS, UNIVERSITIES, COLLEGES, AND PROFESSIONAL ORGANIZATIONS:
Quantity discounts are available on bulk purchases of this book for educational or gift purposes. Special editions or book excerpts can also be created to fit specific needs.

Dedication

The journey of a caregiver is a heroic one, one that calls out of the caregiver a hospitality to serve, to be served and to respond to one in need. It is a hospitality that gives voice to the unique stories of the host and the guest that creates space to welcome and listen to the stirrings within one's Soul

To all caregivers, who tirelessly and selflessly give of themselves, and to all those with whom I have been privileged to serve, and who have taught me to be a caregiver, I dedicate this work. They have shaped and transformed me as a wounded healer in becoming a better and wiser person.

Secondly, I am deeply grateful to my publishing consultant, Brian Schwartz, my editor, Rae McWhirter, and Dennis Patrick Slattery, my literary mentor and guide.

And finally, I want to thank my partner Dr. Nixson L Borah, Ph.D. whose compassion, editorial voice, and support have guided and supported me to make this book possible.

Acknowledgements

I am deeply grateful to, Cindy Atlee, Angela Bellan, Jordan Biaquera, Carol Courcy, Bill Devine, Charles Feldman, Joy Goldman RN, MS, Debra Habr, Valerie Hayes, Beverly Henry, Bro. Richard Hirbe, Deb Humphreys, Julie Inzerillo, Jean Lambert, Paul LaRiviere, Jim Lipsett, Ken Mardian, Pearl Mohnkern, Luis Ochoa MD, Carol S. Pearson, Ph.D., Christina Puchalski MD, Tom Royer MD, Joe Ryan, Jocelyn Scarborough, Carol Schmekel BSN, MHSA, Winnie Stump, BSN, RN, MS, Donna Taylor, and John Zipprich for their support, friendship, and soulful comments about this work.

TABLE OF CONTENTS

The dance between the caregiver's needs and those of the one in need is explored. The chapter is an introduction to exploring something we do every day: to reflect on our experiences.

The question, "What is Soul?" is addressed focusing in how the caregiver is empowered and sustained by going deeper into the inner caverns of one's being and listening to the inner beats of one's heart.

The magical and the universal underpinnings of the role of caregiving, in the broader mythic and archetypal realm of a culture, are examined.

Both the mythos and logos of caregiving is discussed. Each relates to faithless science and unscientific faith leading to a unity of the left and right brain functions.

This chapter explores how the caregiver, as host, experiences three different dimensions of hospitality: hosting the stranger, listening to the story of the guest, and understanding one's interior stirrings.

The ancient question of the frailty of humankind is explored. Within each of us is a space that seeks wholeness and transformation, an area of woundedness which seeks to be heard.

The art of reflection is a fundamental skill for caregivers which implies allowing the moment to take root and to reflect on how to nourish and sustain oneself as a caregiver.

Imagination helps one discover meaning and realize that the essential actions of a caregiver are spiritual.

What is a Practice? Is Caregiving a spiritual practice? These questions are explored as the ordinary becomes spiritual, as inner strengths and values give birth to meaning, insight, and transformation.

Compassion fatigue and its two sisters, secondary traumatic stress and burnout are examined. Caregivers experience compassion fatigue because they care.

Foreword

I had the great pleasure of working with Dr. Edward Smink when he was finishing his requirements in the Mythological Studies Program at Pacifica Graduate Institute in Carpinteria, California. He had taken several of my courses and subsequently invited me to chair his dissertation on the topic that is now *The Soul of Caregiving: A Caregiver's Guide to Healing and Transformation*, a topic that Edward has been engaging for a good part of his professional life. It is a delight to write this Foreword to an important topic that I am certain will be read by and benefit many in the field. But it is also a book that would engage any reader interested in woundedness, affliction, dismemberment, disease, myth, spirituality, healing as well as a host of additional topics.

Caregiving is heroic work, as Edward makes abundantly clear; it is a calling in the original sense of vocation—to be called, called out, called forth and called to. One can, as mythologist Joseph Campbell has written and spoken about many times, hear the call, heed it or refuse it, but if heeded, then one gives oneself over to something far bigger than s/he. Edward answers both explicitly and implicitly what the heroic calls up in each of us that we may, within our capacities, quest after. We might also ask: what is it in the nature of the heroic that an individual, a society, or a culture needs as much as oxygen and food? Yes, it is a call to adventure, but in a specific way: a call to serve, to be in service and that calling, if authentically engaged, leads to a joyful sense of freedom. To serve is to be free. Edward's vision and then recollection of his own heroic journey into the deep wilderness, what Dante called "la selva oscura," the obscure place, that illness, affliction, and woundedness demand the caregiver enter, is not for the faint of heart, or the hard of heart or even the half-hearted.

Vocation can then be a *vacation* in this way: to vacation is to vacate a life that one thought it was his/her destiny to live out; but one may have to vacate that life if one is called to another. None of us can be absolutely sure that their calling is the definitive one, but the heart has a good sense about these things. Edward's own life history had been preparing him for a life of compassion, care-giving and with it, a path to self-knowledge.

I also sense in his words that caregiving is closely aligned with an alchemical enterprise. He tells us early on that "the caregiver's guide is interior; it is about recovering one's Soul." Like the early alchemists of the Middle Ages, who initially thought their work on the world's matter was the goal of their labors, but who eventually discovered over time and in the process that the transformation was less about matter and more about their own psyches' metamorphosis. So, has Edward's work with the wounded, the afflicted, with the diseased, with the dying been similarly concerned with his own Soul's stamina, quality and resilience. These same concerns of course bend towards those he has served as well.

I also enjoyed reading Edward's images from myths and stories that serve as sinews and tendons to the body of his work, holding things together, adding exceptional tensile strength to the entire journey. I was reminded of the power and appropriateness of the goddess Hestia in this context. She is so pertinent to Edward's study for a few reasons.

Hestia combines psychological life, which is the realm of myth and story, with chronological time, the realm of history and human temporality. Her father's name means chronology. Her place in the home is of the hearth and of the warmth conveyed from there. Each of us, but most especially caregivers, carry the warm glowing coals of both hearth and heart within. She is in this regard the energy that warms relationships. She creates and refreshes community, a sense of belonging and of being sheltered. Hestia is also connected to the power of coherence, the presence that allows or helps one to fashion an underlying form to a life and to narratives. In this regard the divine goddess promotes both hospitality and hospice through her hearth fire. She is a presence of hospitality who exercises both patience and restraint. I sense that Edward speaks about her without naming her directly, in his caring role with those in need.

Healing, then, in its caregiving inflections, is an expression of myth making. Both the heroic impulse and the presence of Hestia bend the arc or care giving as a mythic action, or perhaps better said, a mythopoetic action, because healing is a form of *poiesis,* of making or shaping something or someone into a coherent form, which captures the original sense of the word *poiesis.* One does not become afflicted without a mythic transformation on some critical existential level. So too with caregiving; one does not contribute to healing without some corresponding transformation of the healer, which Edward eloquently describes frequently in his pilgrimage through the stories that comprise his journey.

One of many unique insights I found in Edward's exploration is that caregiving in its deepest contours is fundamentally a spiritual practice as he describes it in one of his most provocative chapters. A spiritual life cannot be separated from a care giving life, whether that assistance is professional or personal, and even that distinction feels false. In his writing Edward reveals that psyche, spirit, body, myth and science cannot be separated if one is to be with the one in need fully and authentically. Caregiving is no time to begin to split the person into segments and thus fragment the care one offers. A holism is needed that is both lived deeply in the caregiver and migrated to those as they seek resolution of their lives on multiple levels.

From the above, Edward moves to his last chapter, which outlines the haunting danger implicit in such work: burnout, exhaustion, a dry gas tank, fatigue, bankruptcy of energy, a dry well—all of which are rich metaphors harboring the risks of too muchness in this demanding field. He tells us at one point that "fatigue flattens compassions" and dulls the healer, all of which puts at risk the one seeking and needing healing. Complicating this always-present malady for the healer is compassion itself, which is risky because of where it leads one: into places of pain, wilderness, wounding at times, and the frustrations attendant upon caring but not being able to do much beyond that. Here the implication is that imagination itself can be a blessing and a blister; we care about another, so we take on their suffering, often most cogently through their narratives. This is exhausting work, courageous work and it demands from the caregiver a wisdom about when to let go, back off, let be, so to open space for one's self-care.

Calling time out is as much a part of this noble and strenuous enterprise as any effective work with patients, clients, and those in need. I think it is a perfect chapter to end the discussion, because often it is the last thing we hear in a talk or read in a book that stays in our memory with the most adhesion.

I am not a caregiver in the role that Edward and an entire population engages each day, but I learned so much that is applicable to my own life as a teacher if I have the courage and wisdom to follow Edward's multiple insights. He has reminded me and anyone who reads this fine study that caring for ourselves is a fundamental requirement because it allows us to follow our own destiny with vigor, vitality and a sense of joy.

Dennis Patrick Slattery, PhD, Emeritus faculty in Mythological Studies at Pacifica Graduate Institute and author of The Wounded Body: Remembering the Markings of Flesh and A Pilgrimage Beyond Belief: Spiritual Journeys Through Christian and Buddhist Monasteries of the American West.

Introduction

Reflection on a life of nearly fifty years, as a caregiver in multiple healthcare and leadership roles, gives me pause to seek to find a voice and be heard. There are many reasons why one would want to write a book, and as a caregiver, something within me aches to share the insights and wisdom that I hold as a sacred treasure. I want to reach out to all who care selflessly for others. I want to say that the scars or interior wounds that you experience as caregivers are invitations to rediscover your Soul. You are not alone. You are not going mad when your soul aches because you have cared.

The vocation of a caregiver is a deep archetypal calling that sustains and allows one to enter another's life as no other. In those moments where you hold what seems to be unbearable, you stand firm, maybe with knees shaking, and give life to those in need of your care. In holding what seems to be unbearable, you also experience pain and suffering in your acts of caregiving. Caregivers suffer because they care. Who hugs the hugger when h/she is at their wits end and is often feeling confused, overwhelmed, and even alienated from his or her peers?

Why do so many caregivers downplay the normal reaction to traumatic events or vicarious suffering they experience? Why are caregivers often fearful to reach out to another in confidence, or to share their story that screams to be heard? Why is it difficult for caregivers and for their peers to recognize and support those internal aches that gnaw and throb until the caregiver listens and then takes action? Who among us will listen? Do we know how? Who among us will care and who will be the first to reach out?

These are themes that are explored in *The Soul of Caregiving*. Not to give answers, but to create a space for each reader to listen to, become aware of, and claim their own voice by the power of reflection. This is not a how-to-do-it book, because the guide to caregiving is not about an exterior action. The caregiver's guide is interior, it is about rediscovering one's Soul. It is not a quick fix, but a journey, a pilgrimage. Soul takes one deeper, through the resistances, through one's interior Soul pain and sufferings, to a reservoir of wisdom. Travel any way you like. You can walk, hike, sit on the back of a camel, ride in a rickshaw, or sit on an imaginary magic carpet, as you become a participant in a pilgrimage that is being assembled.

My definition of caregiving is broad in scope and covers a diversity of occupations and professions. Our cast of characters include caregivers in the healing arts, healthcare professionals, physicians, nurses, therapists, health-care and ancillary workers, certified chaplains, certified coaches, spiritual leaders, pastors, wellness coaches as well as first responders including firefighters, safety officers, and emergency medical service personnel. How about active and retired military, educators, and parents who care for their chronically ill children, and adult children who care for one or two parents? We are all caregivers.

This journey is one that is familiar and unfamiliar, one that is laden with surprises, struggles and monsters that appear to challenge us. Interior promptings of the Soul encourage the caregiver to reflect on daily triumphs, challenges, joys, and sufferings. Caregivers experience vulnerability, helplessness, fears, and pain over the traumatic events because they care, because they are human. At its core, the practice of caregiving requires a discipline of the heart, a focus to be present, to listen, and create an interior space of welcome for the one in need. Simultaneously, caregivers are given the opportunity to reflect on experiences, a process that is not foreign, just one that is lost or clouded over by the busyness of everyday lives. These promptings support of Soul, sustain, and empower us as caregivers. This is the *Soul of Caregiving* reclaiming one's interior guide through the process of reflection that leads to healing and transformation.

Chapter 1 - The Dance of Caregiving

Introduction

Most caregivers I know find it difficult to accept thanks for what they do. You often hear them saying, "It was nothing," or "I'm just doing my job." Others might say, "It's my responsibility," or "What am I supposed to do?" or "I am a parent, a spouse, a first responder, etc." Always vigilant, conscious of what has to be done, and preparing for the next task, caregivers are notorious for moving on, often too busy to stop and to listen to what is stirring within. Often many say, "It's too painful to go there." Patterns develop and before you know it, emotions and feelings are buried under layers of personal or cultural taboos that hinder one's capacity to debrief, feel, reflect and heal.

Personal and cultural taboos may include a fear of being vulnerable, or "what will my buddies think if I share how a particular event affected me?" "They may think I am not qualified or able to handle the work." Others may think they will be ridiculed, they are not tough enough, or considered weak. Others are fearful they will be reported for symptoms of PTSD - a real job destroyer. Each profession of caregivers has developed unique and specialized bands of brotherhoods and sisterhoods. Police, firefighters, first responders, healthcare professionals, mothers and fathers, each create and participate in a culture that is uniquely their own. Dr. Atul Gawande asserts that there are three common elements of a profession: the expectation of selflessness, the expectation of skill and the expectation of truthfulness.

He also adds a fourth element that he calls team discipline, such as using a checklist to assure competency and team support for each other.[1]

Each caregiver contributes his or her unique talents and skills to a team as they navigate their own sense of belonging. While a community is developed among team members, that common bond of sticking together at all costs can also limit or prevent those personal interactions that build and foster personal and team growth. It has to do with who belongs, who is in and who is out. The very bond that creates the fraternity and sorority can also cause blind spots for one to be open to other points of view. Caregivers are tough, each representing and perpetuating behaviors that are inclusive and lead to a sense of belonging. Against this backdrop is also the human need to reflect and tend to one's needs, both personally and collectively.

After all, reflection can be dangerous as it is healing for the caregiver. Dangerous, because reflection reveals vulnerability and bottled up emotions which may surprise the caregiver. Cultural taboos and unspoken rules emerge around feelings, around giving voice to what needs to be said, and around developing an attitude of trust. The caregiver learns it is dangerous to feel, because one may uncover hidden, frightening, and unfamiliar emotions. Talking can be risky because words may express something deeper, something more emotional than what one wishes to articulate. Issues that lead to a lack of trust develop around being vulnerable or even being ridiculed over taking a risk, or wanting to express the demands of caregiving, which may fall on deaf ears. Personal and team reflection sort out one's feelings on what needs to be said, and how one learns to trust. Consciously and unconsciously, a narrow passage opens where insight, truth telling, and self-discovery are experienced.

Truth Telling

Reflection is a truth teller. The Soul's voice needs to be heard amidst all the chatter and noise caregivers face. Does the inner pain caused by a pattern of living on the surface of things prompt one to go deeper into the depths of one's Soul? There one finds not only the caregiver's skills, talents, and strengths, but also the caregiver's vulnerability, limitations, fears, and wounds seeking to heal. Michael Kearney refers to these promptings as "Soul pain." He writes, "Soul points us inward and downward to the roots of our humanity and suggests that reconnection with our Soul is the central issue."[2] Reconnection is a process of reflection in discovering one's interior resources hidden within.

When we speak of the Soul, we speak of that psychic energy and life principle that sustains us. The depth psychologist, James Hillman, understands well how Soul leads one to personal healing. Soul pain is about listening to those interior voices that seek to be heard and captures, metaphorically, the angst and the experience of suffering, as well as the invitation and the desire to enter into a journey of healing.[3] Pain sears our Soul when one acts unjustly or unethically. Soul pain can also be something within us screaming to be heard, reminding us that something needs attention.

Examples may be experiencing a horrific traffic accident as a first responder, or anyone who finds himself in a car turned on its side. The emotional strain of life and death situations experienced by emergency room caregivers may eventually take its toll in what is called compound PTSD. Other times one may feel an uncomfortable empty feeling stirring inside. Does anyone hear the frustrations of a parent whose son or daughter is ill, or caught up on drugs and alcohol? Stirring, common to all caregivers, is a sound of Soul pain, reaching out wanting to be heard. Interior walls that are built up for protection can be both protective and debilitating. Like the pomegranate that is crusty on the outside, yet within is a wealth of interior richness. Some walls need to crumble instead of being reinforced. Others need to be created in establishing self-care boundaries. Talking becomes an invitation for reflection to listen to what needs to be addressed.

While reflection is an ordinary experience of being human, and while there are patterns of behavior that hinder this process, the caregiver is like a conductor leading an orchestra, who, while being caught up in the music h/she leads, is still aware of the responsibility to conduct. How often we, as caregivers, are involved in emergent situations when our training takes over to help sort out the crisis at hand? We know that those experiencing crisis situations are often in shock and have difficulty listening and making decisions. Often, we must repeat ourselves, not because of a lack of interest by those affected, but because it is difficult to hear when one is experiencing a crisis. I remember a colleague in ICU complaining about a patient's family member having difficulty in understanding some of the nurse's directions. It became an opportunity for both of us to reflect on how the capacity to hear, and really listen gets numbed when one is experiencing a crisis. We instinctively need to create the external structure for them to be safe and to respond when ready.

A metaphor I often found helpful in explaining this process to caregivers is like a parent, who when a tearful child runs to him or her, reaches out with extended arms to embrace the child. Reaching out with extended arms is another way of saying that we, as caregivers, create that external container of safety and reassurance for those we are called to serve. I remember, being called to the Emergency Room two days before Christmas. A young corpsman, Jose and his wife, Angelica had just arrived in an absolute state of shock. Their baby girl had died. Despite the tragic event unfolding and their need for answers and reassurance, the police were there to rule out any wrongdoing. Imagine the sensitivity needed for this grieving family. They had planned to leave that day to travel to Angelica's family for Christmas.

The grief I felt could not be put into words. Yet, here I was holding what I felt could not be held, orchestrating a family in grief through the legal ramifications of a Sudden Infant Death Syndrome or "SIDS" death. As I sat with Jose and Angelica, tears filled my eyes as I listened to their story. Be strong and yet, compassionate. Be sensitive and aware of one's feelings, and yet, don't let them get in the way of listening and being attentive to their needs. My training had prepared me to recognize my own emotions and not let them get in the way. They did, however, became a springboard affecting my presence and words. While I had learned the importance of debriefing afterward, at the same time, what I was feeling taught me how to respond compassionately. Reflection is a skill that all caregivers have, whether or not we allow those interior voices to surface. As common as the air we breathe, this practice is like anything else that needs practice, it may be lost and not resourced. A dilemma to be sure.

What is Reflection?

At different milestones in our lives, like birthdays, anniversaries, graduations, career advancements, marriages, divorces, and deaths of friends and relatives to name a few, memories flood our consciousness spontaneously for review. Caregivers share in these and can relate milestones in their personal and professional lives. Some of these are painful, others empowering, and some even transformative. These milestones are not in the headlines. The satisfaction of a first responder delivering a baby in the field is scary, while at the same time, is filled with joy. When parents experience their advice heard by a son or daughter, frustrations melt away. The physician who struggles to save a life and succeeds is filled with personal and professional satisfaction. Caregivers often experience moments that feed their Soul. Each of the experiences above is an example of reflection, which is more common than most of us think.

Reflection is a process of stepping back and reviewing one's experience and memories of an event. There are times the caregiver is an active participant, that is, reflection involves the caregiver and what h/she is experiencing. There are other times when the caregiver is an observer, sorting out the details, even if they are part of the event. Sometimes both occur.

Reflection is spontaneous as if one is caught up and lost in the moment. It is a sort of leave-taking if you will. Similar to daydreaming, particularly at dawn and evening tide, reflection takes us to places of wonder and excitement. Other times, reflection needs time to germinate, like a gardener planting a seed in good soil. Often surprised by new insights, one's Soul is active in creating new roots and foliage, as the seed dies to give new life. Do you remember your experience of eating a homegrown tomato from your garden? How about being captivated by the laughter of a child? What about experiencing the birth of your children and your grandchildren? My sister remarked at the birth of her son's twins, her first grandchildren, "I thought I knew what love meant until I felt such love for these babies."

Can anyone remain neutral, observing the wonder of a sunrise or sunset, or allowing a work of art to enter your Soul, equally when music lifts you up like a magic carpet? Life is full of moments that continue to stir within us. I still remember my excitement descending the spiral stairs of the Musée de l' Orangerie in Paris to view Monet's water lilies. What I wasn't prepared for was what I experienced. I felt I was entering a cathedral, a sacred space as I caught a glimpse of Monet's water lily murals covering the oval walls. Purples, shades of greens and blues, swirling amidst shades of cream, white, yellow, reds, purples and pinks captivated me. Water lilies, like stars in the darkening sky, broke through the canvas with a brilliance that captivated my Soul. Time and space vanish in these moments of reverie as we experience something of the infinite and feel a moment of transformation.

A Tree in a Box

Caregivers often get lost in the miracles of healing and the tragedies of life. Each encounter and experience, consciously or unconsciously, changes our perspective on life as we know it. Life has its way of teaching us like stones polished in a raging stream. We remember joyful and painful experiences. Sometimes, we rejoice and sometimes, we are burdened with tragedies we cannot control. Sometimes we fail to ask for help. Sometimes we just feel lost without answers, numb to what is going on inside. These are the moments that give birth to a new insight and an understanding of our own human condition. These moments lead to opportunities for growth and transformation.

The Chinese symbol for tragedy gives some insight about this process. Picture a tree growing inside a box. A conundrum indeed. For the tree to survive, its branches must break through the confines of the box and reach toward the heavens. Likewise, the roots of the tree must dig down, breaking through the box into the rich soil of the earth to survive. Moving upward, branches reach out, roots dig downward to find nourishment. The wisdom of this teaching is as profound as it is simple. The experience of tragedy leads to opportunity. This analogy applies to us as caregivers. While there are many happy events caregivers experience, we also experience tragic situations like a SIDS death, car accidents, attempted and actual suicides, and unexpected deaths to name a few. Caregivers often find themselves betwixt and between. Can these be opportunities for growth? Can we take the risk of feeling, talking, and trusting our personal insights? What within us needs to reach out for help? What within us needs to unearth the strengths that support us?

Granted, in emergent situations, focus on the situation is paramount, as in the example I gave of being a conductor. But what about those in-between times after the event to make time for a post evaluation? Could there be a moment, a reprieve, a quiet time for reflection? Can we give ourselves permission to begin and validate a process of self-care that leads to employee and job satisfaction? Such examples are a job well done, sacrifices acknowledged, tragedies recognized, compliments from peers, families, and clients. Is it safe for the caregiver to express the Soul pain h/she feels after a tragic event? Regardless of the cause that initiates this pain, C.G. Jung suggests "that the function of the psyche is to feel what really needs to be felt so that one may experience the interior resources and helpful powers that are hidden within. Moments of awareness, insight, and self-actualization are waiting to be discovered within us."[4] These in-between times are the moments of self-awareness, insight, and self-actualization. Yet, we feel it is better to move on, which creates the double bind of wanting to sort things out, and at the same time, finding ways to avoid these moments of debriefing and reflection. This creates a tension I like to call the dance of caregiving.

The Dance of Caregiving

The dance of caregiving is living in the tension of not only being present to the needs of the other, but simultaneously recognizing, at least from a distance, what is happening within oneself. Does the very act and responsibility of caregiving distract or deaden these interior and exterior stirrings that embellish the good work that we do? The task of **The Soul of Caregiving** is to address these questions. The irony is, that while caregivers are hardwired in their training to listen, evaluate, and problem solve, these same skills are not applied to their own self-care. The task before us in this work is to discover that we are listening, that we are processing, and that we allow questions to germinate, even if they are painful. Self-care is difficult for caregivers. I know from personal experience, as a survivor of compassion fatigue which led me into the darkness of burnout. I didn't know how to say no and spent little time for myself, as I was too busy helping others. I also didn't know how to build compassionate resilience. I was not accustomed to applying innate skills for my own emotional, psychological, professional, and spiritual growth and well-being. What I was searching for in my acts of self-care was not an exterior action, but one that was sourced in my search for caring for myself. A difficult task, maybe, but not as difficult as remaining in that in-between void of not tending to my individual needs. A dear friend and coaching colleague of mine shared her experience and resistance to the process of reflection and self-discovery. She mused "This work is not for sissies."

An Early Remembrance of Caregiving?

I remember vividly the blood stains of paw marks etched in the snow on the back steps of my house. I must have been six or seven. All I knew was that this abandoned puppy needed help, and I begged my parents to keep him. I cleaned the blood between the pads of his paw, extracted a broken piece of glass and bandaged him up. His name was Sandy, and he became my first pet. This was my first experience of being a caregiver. Amusingly, I wondered throughout the years if this experience was a precursor to my over forty-five years as a nurse's aide, registered nurse, pastoral counselor, executive healthcare leader, and a life coach? I am sure that there are early childhood experiences that may also surface in each of your lives.

Who, then, are the caregivers? We all are, for caregiving is at the core of being human. Our life experiences teach us the art of caregiving for ourselves, for others, and for the community. The art of caregiving transcends any one culture or ethnic tradition, as its arms embrace and reach out to others. Caregiving is about forming relationships with oneself, with others, and with the transcendent Other, as one may discover. Caregiving has universal and archetypal qualities about it and is enshrined in many spiritual and religious traditions. Caregiver specificity lies in the unique roles and actions that caregivers perform. These are skill specific. For example, there is a difference in how first responders, or police, or firefighters care. Likewise, those involved in the healing professions respond and care for individuals according to their needs.

More than a job, caregivers are privileged to enter the mysteries of life such as birth and death, suffering and joy, wellness and illness, healing and transformation. Caregivers are trained to adapt and become responsive to the needs of those they serve. Day in and day out, personally and professionally, caregivers take to heart their unique call that motivates and sustains them. Such was the experience of Katie and Frank whose roles of caregiving dramatically changed when Frank was diagnosed with terminal lung cancer.

Changing Roles

Katie and Frank were married for over forty years. They had grown close together, each caring for the other in their own particular ways. Katie loved to cook, and it was a delight for her to surprise Frank with new and exciting meals. Frank loved to do chores around the house but found it more difficult as he could not catch his breath. He reached out to his son who responded willingly to help with chores and repairs for his Dad. They too were close, as his son spent many years learning different skills from his father. Meanwhile, Frank's appetite slowly began to diminish as his condition worsened. His diagnosis was poor, and he was eventually placed on hospice care.

During one of my visits, while Frank was resting, Katie asked if she could talk with me privately. Her eyes welled with tears. "He hardly eats anything anymore. I don't know what to do? I have enjoyed cooking for him, now he won't eat." Katie was now facing a loss, indeed part of her identity as a caregiver and his wife was in question. Without any warning, Katie began to experience the reality of a future without her husband. Her cooking could not alter his diagnosis. Katie was experiencing what is called anticipatory grief, which Theresa Rando defines as an expectation of a future loss in which normal grief can occur. "It is the process of normal mourning that occurs in anticipation of the death and its consequences."[5] In a later work, Rando explains that anticipatory grief involves three timeframes that are being mourned: the past, the present, and future.[6] Katie recognized that things could not return to the way they were, nor could she deny what she was feeling at the present time, that she could no longer cook for him in the future.

Katie now faced a new normal, Frank's lack of appetite, and her changing role as a caregiver. For Katie, her role as caregiver didn't end, it just changed. The joy of caring for Frank though cooking and preparing meals, now changed. Katie was discovering a new joy in becoming a caregiver of vigil, to midwife her husband one day at a time until his death. The anthropologist, Dr. Angeles Arrien, speaks of caregiving as one of the many mysteries of the universe. She comments that the experience of illness "is an initiation to coming home again to a deeper sense of self and wellbeing."[7] Their relationship built over forty-five years of marriage was the bond that allowed Katie and Frank to care for each other in a such a way that led to their experience of a renewed love, healing and transformation.

The Call

There is a moment when one, consciously or unconsciously, decides to become a caregiver. Beyond expectations or a sense of duty, the caregiver responds to an inner call, or what Joseph Campbell refers to as the call to adventure.[8] Among my colleagues who are in the healing professions, it is interesting to note, that many entered the field because of their own personal experiences of illness or being involved with family members or friends who were ill. Often, police, firefighters, and first responders are equally inspired by their personal experiences and those of generations of their families who have served in these professions. Often, when I ask these caregivers if they consider themselves a hero, their response is "certainly not, just doing my job." Asked differently, if they consider their work to be heroic, there is often a pause, and with some hesitancy, many slightly shake their heads in the affirmative. Something intuitive takes over. Why the hesitancy, and what internal stirrings affirm that the act of caregiving is heroic? The call of entering the landscape of pain for the caregiver and the one who is in need is not an easy task. Compassion requires an inner discipline of heroic proportions, grounded in one's spirituality that has a universal understanding.

A Heroic Adventure

As Campbell suggests, there are a thousand faces, names, and journeys that may articulate the hero. The hero's journey and the call to adventure is one of humankind's universal experiences that transcend time, culture, religious and spiritual traditions. Each day caregivers witness the heroic and courageous efforts of those they serve. They witness the fears, the anxieties, the uncertainties, and the emotional, psychological, and spiritual vulnerabilities of those who seek their services. The invitation of the caregiver to enter into, hold, guide, and sustain one through the mystery and chaos of injury, danger, illness, and even the experience of the death of a loved one takes heroic skills, compassion, and servant competencies. There is no time for a bad hair day, the client, the patient and the one in need come first. Or so it seems.

For the caregiver, the call comes with the decision to enter into the world of the person they serve. Each situation, each circumstance, each person opens up opportunities to respond to one's call. In the ordinary, routine and often mundane experiences of caregiving, there are opportunities that challenge ways of caregiving. The task is often daunting and fraught with mystery, as anyone's experience as a caregiver may plunge them into the landscape of their Soul that may hinder or enhance healing. Living on the edge allows each participant to listen attentively to what is being conveyed in spoken and unspoken words, in images and feelings that emerge, in understanding resistances and challenges.

To enter into the world of one in need means to suffer with them, hence the meaning of the word compassion, Latin for with "com," and to suffer with, "passion." Listening becomes the prerequisite for compassion. Both caregiver and the one in need contribute to re-enacting an ancient drama of healing. William Augsburger describes this as the "interplay" between the caregiver and the one receiving care. Within this relationship, a healing dynamic occurs. The empathy and compassion of the caregiver in being sensitive to the woundedness of the one in need, assists them to discover their own healing resources. The strengths of the caregiver assist the client and vice versa.

Augsburger writes: "When wound meets wound, there is interpathy and compassion: when healing calls to healing, there is awareness, insight, repentance, change, and growth".[9] This unique relationship and the themes of compassion, hospitality, woundedness, and transformation will be discussed in much more detail in future chapters. Three examples of caregivers responding to their unique calls give us pause to reflect on our unique call.

Chosen and Unchosen

Josh was an active and energetic teenager returning with his buddies from a high school skiing trip. About fifty miles from home, the temperature dropped, and the car skidded on what is called black ice and slid off the road. Two of four passengers survived the car rolling over and hitting some trees. One was Josh, who suffered extensive head injuries. In a flash, the normal caregiving experiences of his parents raising a teenager changed to one of keeping vigil over their son in intensive care, then rehab and finally to a skilled nursing home. Years later, Josh continues to be in a coma. This was not what his parents dreamed for him, yet it was a call to caregiving they now struggled to accept. Parental duty alone and the deeper choice of selfless loving care were the choices to be explored. The tension between these choices eventually led to divorce, while each continued to visit and be present for Josh.

Mary had a close relationship with her mother, Anne. They had grown to respect each other and as the years passed, they became friends. Overcoming growing pains and letting go of parental control created a new relationship with each other. They enjoyed sharing their personal stories and adventures and had grown closer throughout the years. While Mary had two other sisters and a brother, Anne and Mary always relied on each other for mutual support, especially when Mary's father died suddenly of a heart attack. As Anne continued to age, she became more and more confused, suffered a severe stroke and eventually needed full-time care. While a nursing home was a possibility, Mary wanted to keep Anne at home and care for her. Being between jobs, and able to work at home, the invitation to become a caregiver was spontaneous and liberating. "It was not out of guilt or a sense of duty that I responded to help my mother. I felt it was because of the love we had for each other."

"I always wanted to be a doctor," Bill told me when I asked why he became a caregiver. He remembered reading about missionary doctors and was influenced by his uncle who was a physician. "It is who I am, what I was called to be," he told me during a coaching session. The irony is that Bill's grandfather died from pericarditis when his dad was only 14. His dad worshiped his father, telling stories about how he used to drive with him through the farms of eastern Pennsylvania transporting milk to a local New Jersey dairy. Bill felt his dad never recovered from his grandfather's death. His dad would come home drunk every time there was an industrial accident at work.

The call for Bill was clear and unambiguous, possibly borne out the circumstances he experienced at home. When asked what sustains him now, after all these years practicing medicine, Bill's response was simple and to the point, "Those, whom I served, taught me many lessons about myself, both professionally and personally." He related that he learned more about his skills, when he needed consultation, and what he learned about his strengths and values because he took the time to debrief and reflect. He also gained insight about his blind spots and shadow parts that needed some refinement and fine-tuning. "When you dedicate your life to healing, those you serve somehow become the physician to you. The relationships I have built have sustained me and in some small way, have made me a better person and physician. I am very grateful."

A Review

What a ride! The dance of caregiving leads one in the thrill of being absorbed in the music, the rhythm, the event, and the interchange between partners. Dancing requires both the relationship each partner brings to the dance, as well as learning the individual dance steps. Remember feeling awkward when you stepped on your partner's shoes? Caregivers need to focus on the unique situation at hand. No room for missed steps. Too much focus, however, often leads to a forgetfulness or a resistance to debrief, reflect, and grow from the experience.

The dance requires reflection during and after the experience. Moments that may need to be postponed, but moments that still need to be unpacked later. Risk-taking is involved. The irony is that caregivers do take many risks for the one in need. How can this skill also be applied to the caregiver's self-care? The dance involves living in the tension of being present to the needs of the other, and at the same time, giving one's self the time and opportunity for tending to one's Soul. The process is not either/or but rather a both/and experience. Moments of reprieve create time and space for caregivers to recall, discover, and renew their individual call to become a caregiver. Each encounter has the potential to become an opportunity, like the tree in the box, a lesson for individual and professional growth.

Listening to one's Soul pain and that of another allows one to enter into the sacred space of healing and transformation. Such listening demands a deeper understanding of Soul and how Soul affects the very nature of the work we do. If our work is what we do, Soul is the animated spirit that inspires how we do it. It is from Soul we find the spirit and energy that sustains us. Chapter Two explores Soul in reference to finding the Soul of caregiving. Fasten your seat belts and make sure your tables are folded and stored, and that your seat back is in the upright position. Chapter Two is ready for takeoff.

Timeout: A Moment of Reprieve

At your own pace, give yourself a moment of leisure to reflect on each question below.

1. Are there any insights that come to mind after reading the introduction?

2. What comes to mind when you hear the word reflection?

3. Is taking time out to debrief, to reflect on your experience, and to listen to those inner promptings something you find easy or difficult?

4. Can you recall one of your earliest experiences as a caregiver? Who was involved? How old were you?

5. Has this experience helped you understand something about your call as a caregiver?

Chapter 2 ~ Reclaiming Soul: Going Deeper Within

Introduction

Soul has the power to move you, consciously or unconsciously, taking you beyond the present moment to a different time and place. There is no remaining neutral or intransigent, as Soul has its way of prompting you. Soul has its own personality, and like a multi-faceted gem, it generates a variety of perspectives, hues of understandings, and a plethora of meanings. Within this new perspective and landscape, James Hillman believes one finds some hidden ground to stand on, a mythical place that gives one a distinct vantage point and perspective.[10] This vantage point allows one to see with different eyes, the Soul's eyes, where insights and perspectives come forth from the internal spring of one's being. Soul becomes a numinous window that opens one to explore new hidden possibilities.

Reclaiming Soul is simply becoming aware of and listening to those promptings of the unconscious that seek a voice. They may be spontaneous and at the same time, they linger. These promptings guide and facilitate a lifetime of discoveries. They need to be discerned and sorted out. These insights may inspire, challenge, cajole and empower. You may ask, "Where does Soul lead me?" Despite resistance, obstacles, uncertainties, and even reluctance, Soul's persistence will lead you where you need to go. Not to worry about being too late in life, the time is always the correct time for you. At this juncture, interior and exterior promptings pose the same question. Soul invites you to choose life and to respond to your unique calling. Humbling and yet, so empowering, you experience yourself as you really are. Not what your parents, spouse, friends, or culture demand or expect, but what you discovered true about yourself. The mirror of your Soul reveals the person you chose to be, similar to what Joseph Campbell suggests is written in the wisdom literature of the Hindu Upanishad: "tat tvam asi, "Thou Are That."[11] Let's now explore the different multifaceted perspectives of the Soul.

Understanding Soul

A Soul Mate

You may have a *Soul* mate, and gosh, think of the memories, those particular moments and feelings that take you to a place where you and your soulmate meet. Meeting without pretense, without judgment, without preconditions was the memory of how Ellen met her *Soul* mate of over twenty-five years at an after 40's retreat. She was asked to pick a partner for an exercise. Remembering how she often was the last to be chosen in the school yard growing up, she turned and asked the man next to her to be her partner. Little did she know that it was going to last more than one evening. Somehow the metaphor of "love at first sight" didn't measure up to their encounter that deepened as the day progressed. Soulmates meet, and time and space vanish. Can you remember one of those moments in your life? Soulmates cooperate in the mystery of supporting the other to be their true selves. Each becomes a mirror to the other in finding one's self. Like the stars that pierce the darkness of the night, you become engulfed, lost but not so lost, in the experience of the meeting. These are soulful moments of reverie that refresh, empower, and heal.

Soul Food

What about the *Soul* food you enjoyed recently at a friend's home? Something lingered, more than the food you ate, with all its aromas, distinct tastes, and visual delights. You found yourself experiencing the living culture the food encompassed. No longer just a meal, but food that feeds your Soul. The meal becomes a culinary delight, captivating your pallet with sensory delights. The name "Soul food" originates from its African American roots, primarily originating in the Southern United States. Often foods that were less desirable became opportunities to be rediscovered and celebrated.[12] Collard and mustard greens, black-eyed peas, beans, and other vegetables are often cooked with ham hock. Fried chicken and fish, pork ribs, and chicken fried steak were more than an individual experience, the event becomes an invitation to join the family and create community. Kwanzaa is such a celebration of honoring family and friends, as well as fostering community. Each of the seven days focuses on one of the seven principles of the holiday: unity, self-determination, collective work and responsibility, cooperative economics, purpose, creativity, and faith. Ritual African-American, Caribbean, and South American recipes laden tables decorated with the African colors of red, green, and black.

Each year, my family gathers around Christmas to recreate a Slavic Christmas Eve ritual meal. The food is simple and the meal represents a coming together to anticipate the stroke of midnight and the celebration of Christmas. Soul food takes on a different meaning as the ritual meal brings the family together as it has for generations past. It is a peasant meal, mushrooms picked from the forest to make mushroom soup. Onions, cabbage, sauerkraut were grown and harvested. Smells of simmering soup and baked goods continue to enliven the event. Stories of the old days of farming and growing vegetables, as busy hands knead flour to make cabbage bread, pierogis, and honey nut cookies. The ritual meal became a time of thanksgiving and of anticipation, a recalling of the story of Christmas, as well as the stories of grandparents, aunts, uncles, cousins, brothers, and sisters. As a young child, I still can remember my grandmother presiding over the meal. The expectation of Santa coming heightened the celebration, as somehow, he remembered to leave a few gifts at Grandma's house. Grandmothers are always the protector of the hearth.

Another example of a ritual meaning filled with Soul is the Passover meal. The meal takes one beyond the present to relive the story of Exodus. Each food has symbolic meaning. The Seder plate contains a hard-boiled egg, a reminder of past holidays and universal symbol of

19

spring and new life, a roasted shank bone represents the paschal sacrifice, Karpas represents the initial flourishing of the Israelites. (parsley), charoset symbolic of the mortar between the bricks (fruit, wine, nuts) and maror (horseradish). The bitter herbs represent the bitterness of slavery, salt water is a reminder of the tears shed during captivity, the matzah, the unleavened bread as there was no time for baking, and wine. The elder asks the youngest, "Why is this night different than any other night."[13] The act "to take and eat," and chewing slowly each morsel of food breaks open new experiences filled with mystery and Soul.

The event is not only relived, but the original event becomes present in the here and now. The barbecue on the 4th of July represents more than ribs, hot dogs, and hamburgers, as does the Thanksgiving meal. Soul is inseparable from the food we eat, no matter how we commemorate the event at hand. Such was the case of planning a surprise birthday party for a dear friend. Sean had reached a milestone in his life, and he would have been mortified to have a party in his honor. That, however, did not stop his partner to be in cahoots with another dear friend who wanted to have the event at his house. The meal had been carefully planned and prepared the day before, and a simple luncheon was the excuse. Imagine the surprise on Sean's face as he walked into the house with 30 well-wishers singing "For he's a jolly good fellow" raising their glasses for a toast. More than a meal, a surprise honoring a dear friend and the invitation to explore and experience the many stories that each guest brought to the celebration, was the real surprise of the afternoon.

Soul Music

Do you remember listening to *Soul* music on your iPhone as you took your dog for a walk? Who led who, and how did walking become so fanciful? Maybe you began to hum. Maybe you began to sing. Was it Jazz or Mozart? Maybe the music led you to a contemplative silence and for a moment, you experienced being lost, but not so lost, a sort of daydreaming as you walked, or you realized you were dancing to that favorite tune and blushed when someone gave you a high five as they walked past you. Just as art is in the eye of the beholder, music contains the music of the Soul. Speak to any professional dancer about how the rhythm, the lyrics, the beat, and how the song itself, captures each cell, each muscle, each limb, one's entire being. What about the gospel choir? No standing still allowed! The lyrics of *"Rock my Soul in the Bosom of Abraham"* or *"Soul of my Savior"* may have transported them beyond the present to those celestial regions of peace and comfort.

Soul-Searching

At another time, you may have done some serious *Soul-searching* over an issue or relationship that needed a new perspective or understanding. Caregiving pulls the Soul in a variety of directions, necessitating the need for reflection that gives one permission for a time to pause, debrief, and celebrate an outcome.

The executive team of a small hospital was unprepared to do a value check on how they functioned as a team. At a workshop exploring the dysfunctions of a team, one member was concerned that there were two or three members that were always late for each team meeting. The facilitator, a regional mission leader, asked if the group would like to address this issue. All agreed, but one member spoke out saying one could never be certain, as the needs of the patients always came first. Clearly a conflict of values, one in providing excellent care, and the other, a desire to strengthen their core value of collaboration and teamwork. Of note, the one who was concerned about the needs of the patients was always chronically late. What was later revealed is that she deliberately came late because she didn't feel the collaborative efforts of the team mattered. It was a time of serious Soul searching.

The facilitator engaged the group in a lively discussion. On the one hand, the group held the ideal that teamwork was important. On the other hand was the dilemma of making a commitment to live out this behavior. Each voiced the importance of teamwork. The group debated endlessly until finally the mission leader entered the center of the circle, and with his foot, drew, what we may call, a line in the sand. I can still remember the determination the mission leader expressed to me. "It was very spontaneous, before I knew it, my foot became a magic marker drawing a line." He then told the group, "if you want to work as a team, we need to start now, sorting out how we can do this.

Otherwise, we are on a fool's errand." There was a stunned silence in the room, a pause, a time of some Soul-searching. Not a conflict of values, but a decision of making a commitment. The pause allowed the group to reflect, each individually, as the facilitator encouraged the silence, a soulful action not only reserved for mystics, monks or hermits alone. These activities of the Soul are found at the heart of being human. Activities of the Soul are not experienced outside ourselves or in activities we may think must be extraordinary. The American mystic, Thomas Merton, maintains that reflection, contemplation, and mysticism reside and flourish most purely right in the middle of the ordinary events of the here and now.[14] Ordinary events, with ordinary people, that later become food for the Soul. Reflecting, waiting for insights to be born requires commitment and patience, and real Soul-searching produces self-confidence and empowerment.

Soul as an Animated Force

Soul, while considered to be an animated force within a person, is often separated from one's humanity, such as early childhood memories of body and Soul, instead of the person whose very being comprises both. S*oul* animates a person, like a work of art, the lyrics of a song, the lines of a poem, the laughter of your grandchild. Sometimes, time stops and the silence of the moment seems to never end. Being *soulful* and filled with *Soul,* may evoke deep feelings about yourself or one that you admire. I was somewhat embarrassed when I was called a "mensch" by Barbara, the wife whose husband was in the Intensive Care Unit. I was called a man with Soul and wisdom, a title of honor within the Jewish tradition. Reflecting now on this experience years later, these feelings still resonates within me, feelings of pride and wellbeing. An honor I continue to appreciate to this day.

Who cannot but pause when one is listening to Mahalia Jackson sing "God Bless America." The song becomes soulful, not only on its own merit, but also because of the soulfulness of Mahalia who is singing it. We are all too familiar with caregivers who really care and love those they serve. *Soul* may also imply the moral or intellectual nature of a person. Something about their character inspires us. To understand the *Soul* of something, like the *Soul* of caregiving, is to enter into those unique stories that animate us and carry us through those difficult moments of pain and grief. Even in those difficult moments, insights may occur that lead us to discover ever newer insights that led to self-awareness and transformation. Relating to these experiences continues to refresh and nourish us.

I cannot forget the time I gave a presentation at a regional meeting for nursing assistants and home-care aides. My topic was "The Spirituality of Caregiving." Throughout the interchange, one consistent theme emerged from the stories of the caregivers. It didn't take long to scratch the surface of what caregiving meant to them, which, because of their spirituality of caregiving, was evident throughout their stories. Somehow, they discovered what motivated and sustained them in their work. It was all about Soul. They acknowledged that they had come to love those they cared for. I came to give a presentation, and they gave me a life-altering experience.

Who inspired you to become a doctor, a paramedic, nurse, firefighter, safety officer, educator, parent, or first responder, and who and what values and meanings continue to inspire and sustain you in the work you do? Who helped you understand the grit of a difficult situation and taught you to remain steadfast, even when everything within you wanted to jump ship? Soulfulness is what is learned that springs forth from the inner resources of one's life. Soulfulness connotes an inner knowledge born out of the crucible of human experience. Imagination and reflection are the Soul's companions assisting one in this process. Known to masters of spiritual direction, soulfulness implies a "felt knowledge," something one learns to trust, comments William Barry and John Connelly.[15] How do you know? Because you know. This is the humble awareness of one's inner truth. This knowledge unites and signifies wholeness.

The Soul of Caregiving

Let's begin to explore Soul in the context of being human. Soul, suggests Thomas Moore, connects one with depth, value, relatedness, heart and personal substance.[16] Notice the multifaceted understanding of the functions of Soul, like the gem radiating different hues.

Depth: Depth is associated with exploring those inner resources of our being that forge our values and beliefs. I like James Hillman's understanding of Soul and how it implies depth. He writes about the field of depth psychology and its direct relationship to the study of the Soul. "We must go deep, and when we go deep, the Soul becomes involved. The logos of the Soul, psychology, implies the act of traveling the Soul's labyrinth in which we can never go deep enough."[17] Soul connects one with depth and when we go deep, our imagination becomes our guide, leading us into the land of mythos, creativity, and meaning.

Values: Values can be personal, cultural, and organizational. Values are personal and give one a sense of identity. They are nonnegotiable, fundamental and often define who we are. We may argue with the values of our parents, until one day we discover their values are our own. They provide focus, direction, and accountability. Values are forged in the incubator of family, culture, and spiritual traditions. They are tested over time, handed down from one generation to the next, but do not become personal until they are freely chosen, a coming of age so to speak. Caregivers often relate to their values and how they align to their unique calling. Each profession has its own code of ethics with a commitment to uphold the code. Caregiving is sourced in service, often at the risk of peril, as is the case of first responders. We immediately recognize their service standing shoulder to shoulder in contrast to those who don't seem to care. We know intuitively when caregivers care and when, for some, it is just a job. For those who have somehow lost the spirit of their calling, it *is* just a job. Their work is suffocated by routine and in some cases, indifference.

Anthony's postoperative experience illustrates how both caregiver and client suffer when caregivers lose their connection to their calling and values. During the night, Anthony ran a temperature and by morning, his bed was drenched with perspiration. A nurse entered the room and hesitantly introduced herself, as she had one foot out of the door. Anthony told her about his bed being wet. "Oh, you are going home today, not to worry." Anthony asked if he could get out of bed to go to the bathroom. He was still hooked up to his IV medication. The nurse nodded yes, and came over and released the bed rail, then preceded to walk to the other side of the room. Being a nurse himself, Anthony knew after lying in bed he needed assistance in getting up to prevent hypotension, dizziness and possibly fainting. Anthony told me how he sat at the end of the bed, dangled his feet, and slowly stood up. As he walked to the bathroom, the nurse left and one of the nursing assistants arrived and asked how he was doing. She was engaging, not like the nurse whose body language was anything but welcoming, almost shell-shocked. He told her about the bed and his concern because he was not going to be discharged for several hours. Within seconds, the bed was remade and Anthony's faith in caregiving was restored by the nursing aid. Later, Anthony learned that the nurse was an agency nurse, not familiar with the routine of the hospital, and whose nurse mentor was sick that day.

Relatedness: Relatedness, a desire to reach out beyond one's self, is at the heart of being human. We yearn to be in a relationship with our environment, with one another, with a partner, friend and the transcendent. The song "No man is an island. No man stands alone" comes to mind. To be human is to be in a relationship with one's self, with creation and others, and with the transcendent Other. Houston Smith speaks about this trinity of relationships and how the Islamic mystic, Rumi, understood this three-pronged understanding of relatedness.[18] For example, if we focus on the transcendent Other, the All One, we will also discover something about ourselves and creation. We may begin our reflection on the beauty of creation, or on our friends or family, and in doing so, we may experience the transcendent Other. Likewise, if we begin to reflect on the miracle of who we are, our real selves, as Jung referred to it, in this reflection we will discover not only something about ourselves, but also something about creation, others, and Other. The very essence of Soul is to be in a relationship.

Heart: Soul is about heart. Don't you just love the Tin Man in the "Wizard of Oz" who laments that he is "an empty kettle and that he could be human if he only had a heart." The sound of an empty kettle seems to proclaim a lack of soulfulness. A loss of what heart is and how it relates to the Soul does make us sound like an empty kettle. We know too often, those involved in caregiving, who lack sensitivity, empathy, and compassion. There is a disconnect from one's heart and one's service that may make us a victim to one of the shadows of the age of reason.

Until the 17th century, the image of the heart and how we have culturally understood it, moved metaphorically from the human heart, which is the center of the person and the core of imagination, to a technological understanding of the heart as a pump. This was the discovery of Harvey in the 17th century, after conducting his first autopsy, as he held a human heart in his hands. This has influenced our understanding of industrialized medicine. Somehow the heart becomes mechanical, and the idea of the sacred and the mystery seems to be lost. Hillman asks how all that the heart symbolizes, such as the courage to live, the center of one's strength and passion, love, feelings, the locus of one's Soul, and sense of person can be held in the hands of the physician or the coroner? He further comments that during this same period, a French Visitation nun, Margaret Mary Alocoque, had a mystical experience of Jesus as the "Sacred Heart."[19] On the one hand, the medical model seems to separate the heart of a person from himself, whereas the archetype of the heart appears in the person of Jesus who communicates his integrated heart's love for humankind. Counteracting the separation of heart, body, and spirit, the Catholic Church begins a devotion to the Sacred Heart of Jesus in the 17th century. The heart is more than a pump.

Personal Substance: Lastly, the Soul is about personal substance, or what the very essence of being human is. It is about who we are. The "who we are" is essential to reclaiming one's Soul. Substance implies a steadfastness of character and the essential nature of one's being. Mary, a nurse I knew and had great respect for, shared this story that only proved again to me her compassion and strength of character. Fear was evident in the eyes of John as he was actively dying. His nurse, Mary, saw the sweat on his brow and the fear in his eyes while administering IV medications. John was the lone survivor of his family, and it was difficult for him to speak. The doctor had been in to see him earlier in the day and told Mary it was just a matter of time. John had decided earlier that he did not want aggressive treatment and a "Do Not Resuscitate Order" (DNR) was already executed and in place.

Mary knew this when she came to John's bedside. She wiped his face with a cool damp towel and freshened his pillow. John smiled as Mary took his hand and sat down next to him. She asked if he was comfortable and he shrugged his shoulders. "Not so good?" she responded. He acknowledged yes in feeling not so good as he came to understand what was really going on. Somehow, no one directly confirmed what he already knew: he was dying. Mary relied on both the clues of John and her extensive experience with dying patients. She asked, "Do you think of dying?" John nodded yes, as tears rolled down his face. Mary smiled, her own eyes a little misty, and gently moved her head to say yes. No need for many words, as each knew what was happening. His fear seemed to melt from his face, as he knew he was not alone. She held his hand between her own and knowing that he came from a Christian tradition, asked if he would like her to say a prayer with him. He smiled and unable to speak, nodded his head, yes.

As she began the *Our Father* prayer, he tried to speak the words as his lips moved silently. When they finished, John had tears in his eyes. Mary promised to come back after she finished her rounds. A chaplain was already beeped and on his way. It seemed like only a minute, yet it was about ten minutes when Mary returned. The chaplain had just arrived to find John lying peacefully in his bed. He had just died. Mary responded to John's need, and yet, one could still wonder, who the real hero was in this journey. Certainly, John found Mary to be a guide and midwife in his journey of dying. Almost thirty years later, Mary continues to talk about her experience with John shortly after she graduated from nursing school.

These multi-faceted characteristics of the Soul radiate their specific hues "that point us inward and downward to the roots of our humanity and suggests that reconnection with depth is the central issue," argues Thomas Moore.[20] Soulfulness connotes an inner knowledge born out of the crucible of human experience.

A Time of Reverie

The music of Simon and Garfunkel "Feeling Groovy" suggests that all will be well if you just "Hold on," meaning you need to slow down because " you move too fast," and when you move too fast, you are not going to "make the moment last."[21] Making the moment last gives one permission to linger, professionally what we may call debriefing, to allow one's self the opportunity to reflect. Lingering is the Soul's way to acknowledge and listen to one's inner dynamics, emotions, feelings, and learnings. First responders know this too well. Nerves of steel, and yet hidden emotions that will later need attention. Here lies the tension, the dance of caregiving as suggested earlier. Reverie involves a time of lingering and a time of dreamy meditation. It is a way of looking at what is real, allowing oneself to entertain these fanciful musings. As the sun brightens each facet of a crystal differently, so does this moment reveal all the different colors and hues that add to the story as a whole. Lingering, suggests Robert Romanyshyn, allows one to experience the "invisible and subtle shapes and forms that shine through the visible, that sustain it and give it its holy terrors and its sensuous charms."[22] Often many caregivers experience the holy terrors coming into consciousness when they face a time of lingering. Walls are built for protection, and as mentioned in Chapter One, they can prevent the normal process of debriefing to occur.

On the other hand, when one acknowledges a job well done and relies on his or her interior strengths, there is a sense of accomplishment of one's values being lived out, and the ability to work with conflicting emotions. On the other side of terrors and fears are its sensuous charms. Another aspect of lingering creates the space to welcome what the Soul wants to reveal. Lingering is similar to an act of hospitality since hospitality is a kind acceptance of things as they are. Understanding this dynamic is explored in Chapter Five: Hospitality, which is about creating space for the other. Three different perspectives of hospitality focus on the caregiver's response to those in need, the stories of those seeking help, and the personal experiences of the caregiver.

Betwixt and Between

You have heard the phrase, "Are you between a rock and a hard place?" Welcome to a deeper understanding of Soul, to that in-between space of betwixt and between. In other words, the Soul has a certain perspective, a special psychic viewpoint that precedes all other branches of knowledge. You know because you know. In this in-between space, the betwixt and between, between the event you just experienced and the psychic energies you are employing consciously or unconsciously, you wait for insight. You wait for discernment. You wait for answers to questions that are still being formulated. In a culture that expects quick decisions and is impatient with the process of reflection, waiting becomes counter cultural. When one least expects it, insights appear.

The Soul of caregiving becomes a process of gathering, a process of understanding and a process of building a foundation in what constitutes for you, the meaning of caregiving. Reclaiming one's Soul is also a process of trusting those interior strengths and insights to appear that feed one's Soul. How does one reclaim what is a numinous reality that cannot be explained but only understood? This is the goal of this chapter, to gain insight and an understanding about Soul. I like the definition of James Hillman that stresses this numinous quality of Soul that inspires religion. He writes that "Soul is an ambiguous concept resisting all definition because of its metaphysical and romantic overtones. It shares frontiers with religion," argues James Hillman.[23]

As such, Soul has a certain perspective, a special psychic viewpoint that gives meaning to caregiving. The Soul of caregiving is what animates one, as a caregiver, to explore how h/she can reconnect with their inner resources, values, and archetypical energies. Each type of caregiving lives in the archetype of its unique form of service. These archetypes are dynamic because they are not only rooted in ancient understandings of human experience, but also are continually redefined throughout the ages. The nurse, firefighter, physician, educator, chaplain, educator, coach, and safety officer of today, while understanding how they carry on the traditions of generations past, adapt these traditions to the present day. Archetypes also live in myths, not only in the collective understanding of a profession, but also in the individual and personal myths each person brings to the profession. This is what makes the study of archetype and mythologies of caregiving so fascinating.

We are now at 30,000 feet and the seat belt sign is off. Take a look out the window, see the heavens above and the earth below. In Chapter Three, we are about to study the universal language of archetypes, how they guide, support and clarify the different characteristics of the caregiver. Give yourself permission to imagine you are on a magic carpet and already you can get an understanding of what an archetype is.

Timeout: A Moment of Reprieve

At your own pace, give yourself a moment of leisure to reflect on each question below.

1. How has your understanding of Soul changed after reviewing Chapter Two?

2. What insights have you discovered about yourself and Soul?

3. Has your understanding of being a caregiver changed? In what ways?

4. How have our reflections of Chapter One prepared you for reading Chapter Two?

Chapter 3 - Once Upon a Time in the Land of Oz

Introduction

Imagination is the cauldron where insights are born and shaped into prototypes. Clay in the hands of a sculptor becomes a bronze figure, and clay in the hands of a Native American becomes a handcrafted bowl, etched with legends and stories. From time immemorial, stories were told through the graphics painted on clay bowls, statues, and figurines. Just close your eyes, and smell the molten bronze being poured into the clay mold, a possible *Thinker* or *Three Shades* by Rodin. Envision the sculptor's wet hands spinning a clay ball into an Acoma Pueblo bowl, capturing centuries of tradition and craftsmanship. The prototype may have been imagined or written down, painted, or sculpted, imprinted in imagination, until it becomes felt in the hands of the creator.

Welcome to the landscape of once upon a time, as dreams become reality. The ancients of yesteryear and the dreamers of today are precision artists in crafting a model, in creating a prototype, a model or an archetype of an original object they envision to create. The image becomes actualized. We are familiar with the word prototype, which foreshadows the original work. Think of designing a new car. How many years before was it just a ball of clay or a draftsmen's sketch that needed the creative imagination and skill of the artist, to become the prototype for the new car of the year.

I don't ever remember hearing a major auto dealer advertising a new archetype of car, and yet, prototype and archetype mean the same. Archetypes, while hidden from our vocabulary and everyday use, are more common than we expect. Imagine when you hear the song "When you wish upon a Star" or wandered with Dorothy and her companions down the yellow brick road searching for the City of Oz. Do you think of Jiminy Cricket or Toto, the tin man, the scarecrow, or the lion? Each is an example of current archetypes common in the movie industry. Time for us to board the imagination train. We are entering the land of Oz, and what is "Oz?" Is it a make-believe place, a city on a hill, or a land of peace and calm? One word, with a thousand meanings. Such is the nature of an archetype.

Understanding Archetypes

To begin our discussion about archetypes, I found the definition in the Oxford American Dictionary and Thesaurus a good starting point. Its definition states that an archetype is "a primitive mental image inherited from man's earliest ancestor and supposed to be present in the collective unconscious."[24] Images are what the imagination creates and being primitive, they originate from deep within. These images are both personal and collective. Personal, in that, they are born from our own Soul, and collective, because many of these images are universal and shared with previous, current and future generations. Images lead one to explore and to allow one's imagination to soar. Imagination is the primal force and basic reality of human life, argues Roberts Avens, in *Imagination is Reality*.[25] Furthermore, imagination becomes the creative activity of the psyche and Soul, as images often appear before words. Anne and Barry Ulanov maintain that imagination "comes into play in all of our ways of being, in our thinking and feeling, in our intuiting, and our sensing. It expresses psychic life, which speaks first in images before it speaks in words."[26] Images are full of metaphors and meanings.

A Jungian Perspective

The second definition in Oxford Dictionary gives a Jungian perspective that I will continue to develop in this chapter, especially regarding the archetypes of the caregiver, the hero, and the wounded healer. Jung stressed that an archetype is a primordial image,[27] one that constantly recurs during history. An image that has a remnant of the joys and sorrows repeated countless times in our ancestral history. He continues to write that archetypes are those "factors and motifs that arrange the psychic elements into certain images, characterized as archetypal, but in such a way that they can be recognized only from the effects they produce."[28] Does this feel like trying to nail gelatin to a wall?

On one hand, we can recognize the effects of an archetype, such as the universal archetypes of motherhood or fatherhood, and on the other hand, each of these archetypes cannot be captured by time or space. Culture, history, personal beliefs, and myths influence what is understood by each archetype, such as a moment in time, something to cherish, or changes that are enshrined in memory. Yet, each time one experiences motherhood and fatherhood, the experience of the archetype is different. A mother or father gazing at their firstborn is different than when they reflect on their roles as their child takes his first steps, or blurts out her first words, or enters preschool, and all the other milestones in the child's life. Think of Heraclitus and his theory of constant change. Each time one crosses a river, the water flowing underneath is constantly changing. What remains constant is the river.

Understanding the Archetype of Caregiving

I learned caregiving early, in a family of alcohol dependency. In an alcoholic family, there are many roles each family member chooses. Mine was as placator, the informal peacekeeper. My earliest recollection was caring for my dog, Sandy. I learned to be a caretaker, quite different than being a caregiver, which followed me into my adult life. I became overly hypersensitive, indeed, hypervigilant to others needs, often neglecting my own. Despite these patterns continuing, there were moments of excitement and enthusiasm in my career as a registered nurse, pastoral counselor, and executive team leader. There were, however pitfalls and struggles. Midway in my career, I experienced compassion fatigue with one of its sisters, burnout, which is called compound PTSD. It was then I learned the importance of self-care, removed myself from a painful living situation, changed my career and gradually recovered. My experience of over forty years in healthcare taught me much about the difference between caretaking and caregiving, the former depletes one's energies, while the latter sustains and enlivens. More on this later.

We are All Caregivers

My approach to caregiving is broad. In a way, we are all caregivers. Spouses who care for each other, parents who care for their children, or the adult child who cares for a parent, healthcare professionals who care for those they serve, the military and veterans who care enough to provide us with protection and safety, and the selfless dedication of first responders putting their lives on the line. I remember a picture of a firefighter holding a child he rescued, and the smile on his face mirrored the compassion in his heart. The call to duty is enshrined by the first responders who perished to save those trapped in the twin towers in New York on 9/11. How about the police officer who intervened in a domestic violence case and provided safety for the family? We often forget how much they care about keeping us safe, such as the paramedics who are the first responders in traffic accidents. I remember one in particular who helped me get out of my car when it turned on its side. I have no idea how I got out, I only saw his hand reaching toward me as I loosened my seat belt. Again, we are all caregivers. Caregiving is who we are.

Strengths and Shadows of Caregiving

The pioneering archetypal framework of Dr. Carol S. Pearson, Ph.D., articulates the archetype of caregiving to a tee. Her framework identifies twelve patterns of meaning and motivation (archetypes) grouped into four leadership domains that create a story-type profile of an individual and/or a group. These leadership domains are making things work; Getting results; Working with others; and Learning and Adapting. What becomes obvious is how the archetype of the caregiver addresses making things work, by focusing on security, stability, and safety. A detailed summary of the Pearson-Marr Archetype Indicator ((TM) can be found in the reference.[29]

To gain more insight into the archetype of the caregiver, let's imagine you are a producer of a movie. Sit in your director's chair, grab your megaphone, because we are going to direct a movie, similar to Batman, Wonder Woman, and Superman. Action!

Cameras! Roll! If we were going to produce a movie about the caregiver, Dr. Pearson suggests the caregiver's story would contain a plot focused on how the caregiver makes a difference by helping someone in need or in jeopardy. Do you feel the urgency to jump in and experience the adrenaline rush? What happens if there is not an immediate need to fulfill? I remember visiting the cardiac care unit one day, when the census was low due to some discharges, and the staff were enjoying a little reprieve. They were bored out of their wits. One nurse looking up from a magazine said, "Could I pray that we would get more patients. "Pray," I said, "that more people get heart attacks? I said enjoy the rest. It will be busy before you know it."

The Star Attractions: The leading role in our movie would be the selfless caregiver who makes sacrifices to help others. Who would fill this role? Dr. Kildare? Clara Barton? Florence Nightingale? Doctors without borders? Maybe you? Sound familiar? Maybe Mother Teresa of Calcutta, Bill and Melinda Gates, or the home care aid that came to visit when your mother was on hospice. What about the single mom, or the parent that cares for a chronically ill child. All are examples of selflessness, caregiving and compassion. We have the plot and the leading character. So, how would it end? Simply, there would be a happy ending, because people are helped and of course, show their gratitude.

Can you hear and feel the applause, the gratitude of those being rescued? Are you ready to go on stage and receive your academy award? Archetypes take us beyond the present moment into a future of many possibilities. Yet, how often do most caregivers find it difficult to accept compliments? "Just doing our job ma'am" as detective Friday would say on the Dragnet TV program.

Interesting too, is how these three actions, creating a plot, the list of leading characters, and the outcome are similar to the hero's journey as outlined by Joseph Campbell in his classic, *The Hero with a Thousand Faces*. Essential to the hero mythology is the journey of descent, initiation, and return. Campbell captures the universal symbolism interwoven in world mythologies of the hero and the heroic journey, by metaphorically describing the hero as multifaceted. There are thousands of faces, names, and journeys that may articulate the hero. The hero's journey and the call to adventure is one of humankind's universal mono-myths that transcends time, culture, religious, and spiritual traditions. He amplifies the journey and the different tasks a hero can undertake as he writes: "A hero ventures forth from the world of common day into a region of supernatural wonder; fabulous forces are encountered and a decisive victory is won; the hero comes back from this mysterious adventure with the power to bestow boons on his fellow man."[30] The call of the hero, the work, and journey of the caregiver, and then the reward for one's selfless achievements.

Values: What values would you have the leading characters of your movie portray? We already know about personal sacrifice for the good of others. Would you attribute dedication, generosity, and service as hallmarks of their caregiving? Besides demonstrating their professional skills, would you also want them to show their human side of nurturance and compassion? An example may help. The doctor was concerned about the deteriorating condition of one of his patients in the intensive care unit. I remember asking him, "How is Mr. Ling doing?" He told me Mr. Ling was going to die. He was going into multi-system failure due to a massive stroke. Ethically challenged, the doctor who was of Chinese descent, realized any more aggressive treatment would be futile. He asked me to arrange a family conference.

The family was aware that everything possible was being done in the hope that their father might survive. He began speaking to them about their father's condition, that despite all that was being done for him to remain alive, he was in the process of dying. He was also aware that the family requested that all should be done to save his life. Gently and compassionately, the doctor said, "I know in our Chinese tradition, it is wrong to desecrate and dishonor the dead. When your father's heart stops, if we do cardiopulmonary resuscitation (CPR), I believe we would be desecrating the dead, because we have done everything we could, and when his heart does stop, it means your father will be dead." Because the doctor took the time, identified with the family because of his Chinese heritage, the family agreed to follow the doctor's recommendation for a do-not-resuscitate order. Later that night, Mr. Ling died peacefully surrounded by his family. The doctor responded courageously to the need, traversed through the challenges of his treatment options and the responses of the family, and achieved an outcome that served the patient and the family, while being committed to his oath as a physician, do no harm.

Shadows: Day in and day out, we caregivers act heroically in our work. But before we swell up with too much grandiosity, what about the pitfalls of caregiving? Now take a deep breath, as we set the stage for the academy award for caregiver bloopers. Who wins the prize for martyrdom, when one's caregiving doesn't recognize one's boundaries and limitations? What about the enabler, whose wife celebrates her husband's sobriety by hosting a cocktail party? Or the nurse supervisor who puts up with the dysfunctional behavior of one or two of her staff so as not to make waves?

I remember a situation in which we were doing some focus groups around increasing patient satisfaction. The staff involved felt that about 90% of the team was dedicated to such improvement, but there were a few very negative workers on the staff. I asked if this was the total responsibility of administration and HR to deal with or is there something that they could do individually or as a group. The strength of a group usually helps support its members and assists each individual in developing a sense of belonging. If the group puts up with negativity, the group is responsible in at least passively supporting these behaviors. On the other hand, if the group address these behaviors as a group, those causing the disruptions would find they have no audience to vent their frustrations. They would either adapt or resign. One of the staff was concerned that this would be difficult.

I asked why. "Well, if we confront the negative behavior, we might lose that person as our friend." My response was simple: "With friends like this, do you need enemies?" It was difficult for them to see that, as a group, they were sabotaging their own efforts. This was the task at hand, and eventually, with the support of administration, they were strengthened in their resolve to focus on their group strength to help facilitate change.

How many caregivers suffer from vicarious suffering and compound PTSD, and find themselves lost in the confusion of terrifying emotions cascading into consciousness where one more incident is just too much to endure? What about a spouse suffering from PTSD, whose family is trapped in a codependent relationship, not knowing what to do? Who is there to help them? Who will get the award for a lack of self-care because of their need to take on too much, or their feelings of invincibility? I have often remarked that while we caregivers are involved in godly or sacred acts, we are not God, and don't we just love those caregivers who think they are? Who are the people pleasers who often say yes, but really mean no and eventually build up resentment or guilt-tripping, mild depression, compassionate fatigue, and burnout?

Caretaker or Caregiver

Caretaker or caregiver, that is the question. Caregivers are skilled at stuffing down their feelings and reactions to emergent situations. In fact, they are trained to do so. Something, however, gets lost in their efforts - themselves. The joy of caregiving becomes the task of caretaking. Listen to the difference. Caregiving and caretaking. One seems relational and life-giving, and the latter seems task-oriented and depersonalized. If my work simply becomes a task and often becomes a mind-numbing routine, something of the Soul is lost. Lost because the shadows of the caregiver take over and become the caretaker.

In addressing vicarious trauma that can lead to compound PTSD, one may experience compassion fatigue or one of its sisters, burnout or secondary stress disorder. Then, one may ask: "How does this suffering begin?" This is the subject of our concluding chapter, Chapter Ten. How many fires does a firefighter endure before the next fire becomes too much? How many deaths in the emergency room do trained physicians, nurses, and healthcare workers face each day, or one too many extra shifts, or how many violent pursuits do police officers respond to, until one too many incidents, like a straw breaking a camel's back, out of nowhere, one more is just too much and they become the wounded healer?

Yes, that is what happened to me. For three years, I was involved in a leadership development program for a non-profit charity. The winds of change were stirring, yet the organization was split down the middle, half wanting to go forward, and half resisting. Looking back, I did not take care of myself, nor did I realize this may be an impossible task. The whirlwind took me by surprise. There was little time for days off and balancing other responsibilities, which I could have easily delayed or reassigned. The leaders of the program were also nagging me when I wanted to take some time off. "Like, who has time for a short vacation?" I was told. There was an attempt at conflict resolution, and I thought we were making some progress. Somehow, I dismissed the internal conflict going on in me. I thought I was invincible, a not so rare disease for caregivers. I had forgotten that even Superman had his Achilles heel, kryptonite. A lack of self-care was mine. I lost my balance in the work and clouded over my natural instincts for caregiving. I had become a workaholic, but something was nagging at my gut. Until one day, it was too much. I became the wounded healer.

Tears for Spaghetti Sauce

I was one of three directors at a leadership conference where the participants were asked to bring a potluck dish for lunch. It was sort of a community-building effort. I was late as usual, putting the final touches on the spaghetti dish I was preparing, so I went to the kitchen to finish up. In the midst of stirring the sauce, tears welled up in my eyes. Before I knew it, they became sobs, then a torrent, I broke down crying. The floodgates opened as I wailed and bent over in anguish. I knew I needed to add more water to the sauce, little did I expect it would be my tears. I had had enough. There were too many conflicting events and situations, some bordering on abuse, some lack of appreciating my contribution, and my own personal understanding of my personal boundaries. My inability to say no, and my need to take on more than I could handle finally brought me to tears. The well of caregiving within me had run dry. Shaking, I was just able to tell the coordinator I was not feeling well, and off I went. I guess someone else served the spaghetti.

I knew a kind pastoral counselor and began a discovery of recovery. I was suffering from compassion fatigue along with its two sisters secondary traumatic stress and burnout, which I now understand as compound PTSD. I thought PTSD was for those experiencing combat. Yet, according to the national center for PTSD research, trauma can lead to PTSD for a variety of reasons, such as domestic violence, child sexual or physical abuse, terrorist attacks, physical or sexual assault, natural disasters such as hurricanes, earthquakes, tornadoes, floods, fires. First responder witness to traumatic events like a serious accident, a car crash and violence, such as being witness to a robbery or violent attack are other examples of traumatic events. Again, the individual either experiences it themselves or are a witness to terrifying acts done to others.[31] What I had in common was an experience of traumatic events over an extended period of time. While there were no physical guns, bullets or bombs, there certainly were incidents of trauma, resentments, conflicts, unattainable expectations, and emotional abuse. I learned the importance of self-care, removed myself from the painful living situation, changed my career and gradually recovered.

The Loss of Perspective

Something feels heavy when you are a caretaker. There is a sense that something is out of balance, and there is a loss of perspective. Adult children may feel this way when they become caretakers of one or both parents. Obligation gets in the way of caregiving. Boundaries become blurred. Often the brunt of caregiving becomes the responsibility of the female sibling(s) rather than a shared responsibility of all the children. It becomes a breeding ground for resentment. A caretaker may also be a perfectionist who needs to get everything done for others, and by doing so, neglects one's own issues and needs.

Years ago, I remember reading a book called "Addicted to Perfection," by Marion Woodman. The focus, as I remember, is that our addiction to perfection comes from a need to prove ourselves, to get it right, to fill in a gap of believing we are good enough, to do it right so we *can* be loved. This compulsion, Woodman argues, comes from a hunger for spiritual fulfillment. This need, however, gets sidetracked in seeking illusionary ideas of perfection.[32] What seems to be lost is one's connection with one's inner values and strengths. Listening to Soul gets dulled and lost, the very thing which is the core of one's spirituality.

The question then becomes, "Is one able to shift from caretaker to caregiver?" Cindy Atlee, of the Storybranding Group, teaches an exercise based on the "paired opposites" as described in Dr. Pearson's framework to help with that. It is about creating balance for the caregiver/caretaker by allowing room for the strengths of the hero archetype to emerge and relieve the inner tension created by too much reliance on Caregivers. In my career, I have found that most caregivers have difficulty considering themselves a hero. Yet, when I pose the question differently, asking if they think their work at times is heroic, they shake their heads in agreement. Think of the heroic actions of a firefighter rushing into a burning building, or the risk a police officer takes in apprehending a criminal. What about the parents of a chronically ill child who, day in and day out, find the interior compassion needed? The hero in each of us seeks to make a difference, to triumph over wrong, to meet an existing challenge. Think of the strengths and values of a hero: determination, courage, discipline, energy, principled action and giving your all.[33] So here is the dilemma. In the midst of the struggle, how does one recognize the shadow side of caregiving, and activate one's hero's strengths? How many times does one need to be knocked off one's horse to realize a move is vital to recover from existing as a martyr, to one who can set boundaries and regain one's life? And if the family dynamic leads you to the role of an enabler, how does one use those same energies to care for one's self? That's the mystery of it. The same energies that help you survive, are the same energies that help you live.

On a Raft Surrounded by Sharks

This was a new insight for me. While attending a class for my masters in Counseling Psychology, the professor related story of how, when one starts his or her personal journey, it often feels like being on a raft surrounded by sharks. He asked us to imagine a time when we felt this way and then gave us butcher paper and markers to draw such a time. I drew a broken whiskey bottle and reflected on being raised in an alcoholic family. As I mused in how I had survived, and how I had used so much energy to do so, I consciously became thankful for these energies and said to myself, "Now I want to use them to live." I no longer needed to be surrounded by sharks on a raft. I found a way to go fishing instead.

Conclusion

Our journey of once upon a time in the land of Oz is coming to a screeching halt. For a moment, we were able to get a glimpse into the land of archetypes, into the land of imagination, images, and incarnated dreams that give substance, motivation, and empowerment to who we say we are, as caregivers. In each of these images, Jung writes, "there is a little piece of human psychology and human fate, a remnant of the joys and sorrows that have been repeated countless times in our ancestral history."[34] Archetypes allow us, as caregivers, to experience belonging to a collective group larger than ourselves. There is a certain mythos that binds us to a group and whose membership gives us some standing in the agency and organization. I am a nurse, I am a physician, I am a chaplain, a firefighter, a police officer, a teacher, a mother or father, gives meaning to the "I am," that I am. In Chapter Four, we will explore the mythos and logos of caregiving and how the left and right parts of the brain support each other. So, get ready to explore how the caregiver creates a balance with the skills h/she has learned and the human aspect of experience and reflection.

Timeout: A Moment of Reprieve

At your own pace, give yourself a moment of leisure to reflect on each question below.

1. How has your understanding of the archetype of the caregiver strengthened your resolve as a caregiver?

2. Can you give some examples of when you found yourself relying on these strengths?

3. What are your dreams about your profession? What gives you hope? What discourages you?

Chapter 4 - Truce and Consequences

Introduction

What if there were a truce between the right and the left hemispheres of the brain? What if these two very opposite functions really worked together? What would be the consequences if a balance or harmony existed between the mythos and logos, between the rational and the creative functions of the brain? Do they work separately or together? While the parts of the brain have different functions, they are designed to work together, as both halves play important roles in logical and intuitive thinking, in analytical and creative thinking.[35] Not either/or, but both/and, in this in-between space where one discovers their calling. I like this space, a space of reflection and insight, a place beyond autopilot that most caregivers experience. James Hillman asserts that within this space of questioning and discerning, is the discovery of one's individual destiny that is "between faithless science and unscientific faith."[36]

The Logos and Mythos of Science

Listen to these words of Hillman again as they capture the essence of this chapter. "Faithless science; Unscientific faith." This was brought home to me when I was taking a class in anatomy and physiology in my nursing program at Newton Junior College. The red marks on my first lab report could have been etched in blood as far as I was concerned. The C minus did not register well with me. I felt deflated. I thought I had done such a great job. Were these just illusions of grandiosity? There seemed to be more red ink on the page than what I wrote. The uneasiness continued and found its way to the pit of my stomach. So, what was I going to do? Languish in self-pity, be the martyr, rally against the unfairness of the grade, or join a twelve-step program for students who felt they were victimized? Maybe that twelve-step program could be called Misery-a-holics.

I can't remember the exact moment when my left brain took over and simply asked the question "What are you going to do about it?" Then the right side of the brain suggested that I be creative, as there are many possible solutions. Anything would be better than playing the victim. What did I need to learn? What was the scientific method all about, and how could I apply it to future lab reports? I remember looking at each part of the report that was underlined in red and made a note, as the blood was dry by now, maybe even coagulated. As I went through the report, I recognized that the professor would ask a question or add a comment. She didn't have to do this, I thought. Each question and each note became the ladder for me to climb out of the hole I imagined myself in.

The Inquiry of Science

The scientific method is a body of techniques in how science is carried out. A hypothesis is created, and the method of inquiry follows observation, measurement, and experimentation. This is the natural faith that the scientist uses to analyze the hypothesis through testing and hopes for a predictable outcome. No transcendence here. The left-brain functions of analytic thought, logic, language, science, and math are alive and well.[37] Yet, even in these moments that seem devoid of emotion, holistic thought, intuition, creativity, art, and music, are not these same scientists at awe when they trip upon something new, something unexpected, something laden with mystery that brings them to pause and reflect in what cannot be rationally explained? Welcome to the land of liminal space, the betwixt and between, a space of numinosity and mystery, which if left unexplored, diminishes one's balance and perspective leading to unfortunate consequences.

Tilly Was Her Name

Tilly was her name, a name that summed up who she was as a professor. She was full of enthusiasm and passion about her teaching, with credentials in both science and the arts. Words were metaphors to her, and she would expound on how they brought life to science. Colorful, I would describe her. Who would challenge us to move beyond the scientific fact, to the mystery related to it? The marriage of faithless science and unscientific faith. In exploring the skeletal structure of the human body, her premise was "Function dictates Structure." She asked the class, "Why is there a bulge at the end of the femur, an area filled with spongy looking crevices, and how is this replicated in ancient and modern architecture?" The function of the bone is to carry weight, as are the various arches of a building. The more crevices, the more the weight can be distributed. Just look at the aqueducts of old, the ceilings of ancient times, the arches that distributed weight. The function to carry weight dictated the structure. Even reminiscing about her, I chuckle over how much fun the class then became. Every other report was an A or A plus. Instead of being etched in red pen on paper or curdling blood as I imagined, the recommendations were carried by a company of neurons to be stored in my brain.

Faithless science: the logos, logical, rational, linear, sequential, concrete processing, and verbal. Unscientific faith: the mythos, the creative, the intuitive, the nonverbal, symbolic, random and holistic processing.[38] Focusing only on one or the other leads to an imbalance or lack of perspective. Two examples might help in exploring this dilemma. Julian was a regional director of finance for a large health system. When it came to numbers, balance sheets, and meeting deadlines he was at the top of his game. Dressed impeccably, color coordinated socks, tie, and shirt contrasting his blue or gray suit, he was tidier than his desk. Damn, if only my desk could be as neat. He reminded me of a professor who taught statistics. The only thing we could have on our desk was our notebook, our text, and a pencil. Crisp, clear, and clean, I remembered.

The Task of Self-Care

As part of Julian's on-boarding to the company, I was assigned to be his coach. When we began to discuss his goals, he told me he was asked by the CEO to explore his people skills. People skills, as in relation to non-linear thinking of which he was a master task organizer. People skills, as in building relationships and interactions. People skills that are related to his own self-care. The rationale of his CEO was that if he could understand how his own development of self-care would affect how he approached his staff and work, this would lead to a greater understanding of his peers and direct reports. To Julian's credit, he concurred with the CEO that he needed to explore how to develop his people skills. When he did take time to listen to what he was feeling, he recognized that lacking a sensitivity to his own needs caused a dull ache within him. He, in a way, was fortunate, for unlike so many others, he was aware of his own "Soul pain." Something was out of balance. He wanted (well, sort of wanted or was hinting at) to explore the relationship between developing goals around promoting his own self-care and how this affected his relationships at work.

As Julian and I were discussing his coaching goals, I introduced him to an article by Lisa McQuerrey on *What are Good People Skills*. Lisa best sums up these skills, which include the ability to listen, communicate and relate to others in a personal and professional way.[39] These skills extend to problem-solving abilities, empathy for others, and a willingness to work together towards the common good. We also explored some characteristics of self-care: it is not selfish, helps to prevent burnout, builds relationships and makes one more effective. His homework was to review this article for our next session. Notice the interplay of the two horns of the dilemma for Julian: on the one hand, faithless science to get the job done, sacrifice all including self-care, and his subsequent lack of focus on building relationships, which affected his people skills and on the other hand, unscientific faith, the Soul pain that was gnawing from within to make a difference.

A metaphor for this dilemma is a person locked within a prison cell. Instead of choosing to open the door, oh and by the way, he has the key in his hands, he paints the bars of his cell gold, believing that staying in prison is less painful than choosing to leave it. The opposite of course is true as Julian spoke of his "Soul pain" while remaining in his workaholic prison.

In Julian's case, he needed to take one step at a time. He found it very difficult to take time for self-care. It conflicted with his worldview at the moment. As much as he wanted to get started with coaching, there was always an excuse. Missing scheduled appointments, not doing the agreed upon homework, he gave one excuse after the other in not working on the goals he had created. During one of our conversations, I guess the stars were in alignment. With all the red herrings filling the basket of my consciousness and my desire to turn on the fan because of the smell, I resorted to tough love.

Several core competencies for my certification with the International Coaching Federation, of which I am certified as an associate coach flashed before me: powerful questioning, direct communication, creating awareness, and designing actions.[40] "Julian," I asked, "What I am experiencing is a lot of excuses, or what I call red herrings. It is one thing for your company to assign a coach to all executive leaders, and for your boss to particularize his concern about developing your people skills, but coaching is most effective when you see the value of it for your personal and professional growth. In other words, do you really want to do this? Are you willing to explore with me the "why" of your procrastination about taking steps to work on your goal of self-care? Are you willing to see how this relates to the understanding of your relationship to your own growth, as well as how it also relates to developing your people skills? It is all about relationships."

There was a long pause, and I knew there was a risk of Julian running down the hall telling his boss he did not need coaching. Yet, I knew intuitively from my previous discussions, this was not the case. Finally, Julian caught his breath and said. "I'm very task-oriented and I like to get things done." was his reply. This was faithless science, a mathematician to the core. Yet he went on to say, he has a daily morning devotion that he does before coming to work. Another task on the list, I thought at first. Then he told me that he reflects on the tasks that need to be accomplished for the day. His voice animated as he shared how much this daily devotion exhilarated him and gave him a perspective about his work, something he learned at his church. Julian then related the reason why he chose the company he was now working with. "I was impressed with their values and knew that I could be at home here because of my own."

So, now we are dealing with unscientific faith. I tried not to fall off my chair, as I was so pleasantly surprised and delighted. I got more than I bargained for from these direct and powerful questions. I had to put aside the temptation of fluttering my feathers like a peacock. It was not about me, but about Julian. "Julian, I must admit, you pleasantly surprised me. I am delighted to hear how your devotion animates and directs the work that you do. This is precisely the hope of your parent organization. May I make a suggestion? Why not make self-care one of your daily tasks? Your daily devotion is an indication that you do cut out time for self-care. Can you explore more ways?" A light bulb went on. He could add self-care to the list of his daily tasks. It worked. Julian learned to integrate his task-oriented skills with the creative and intuitive part of his brain. His co-workers and peers started to recognize a difference in how he related to them. He found the key to unlock the door of the prison he created, and now enjoyed developing this new skill.

More Than a Late Report

Sarah is another example. In her role as a Director of a large non-profit, one of her employees, Maria, a star achiever, failed to give a report when it was due. Sarah was perplexed as this was very unusual, as Maria, who recently came to the company, interviewed well and had great recommendations. Hiring highly skilled, professional women was one of the company's objectives, as well as Sarah's. In one of our weekly coaching sessions, Sarah asked how she should approach the situation. My immediate response was to ask what some of her options were.

Her first response was to call Maria in and tell her how disappointed she was with her performance. Linear thinking at its best, job not done, why not? Yet, as she would realize later, there was a subconscious reason at play which added to her disappointment. Maria did not seem to fit Sarah's expectations of hiring a professional woman. This was a learning for Sarah. The realization that she had to put this aside to fully evaluate what was going on in Maria, and not herself became apparent. However, Sarah did mention that she was personally concerned about Maria and wondered if there was something else going on. Sarah began to think her first approach didn't fit. So, what was she going to do next? We agreed to brainstorm what might be an appropriate intervention.

Sarah genuinely cared for Maria. Yeah for the right side of the brain! I suggested she make an out-of-the-box executive decision to show her concern in a simple gesture. She decided to walk down the hall and visit Maria in Maria's office. "Maria," Sarah asked as she knocked on the office door, "May I come in." "Yes, of course Sarah, please come in." Maria didn't expect Sarah to come and visit her. Sarah asked if she could sit down, and briefly discussed the report, then asked: "Maria how are you doing?" This question took Maria off guard, as she was expecting a reprimand. While appreciating the warmth of Sarah's concern, she was unable to allow it to sink in. Maria mentioned that things were tough, but that she was ok, to which Sarah simply said, "I care about you, and I want you to succeed. Let me know if there is anything I can do," and returned to her office.

The next day, Maria knocked on Sarah's door and asked to speak with her. "Yes of course," Sarah responded and stood up to greet her. "Please sit down over there and I will join you." They both sat in some chairs next to a small table laden with fresh spring flowers. "Sarah, when you came by yesterday, I expected you to write me up and give me a reprimand. Instead, you warmly asked me how I was doing. I was caught off guard and needed more time to think it over. I needed to sleep on it and what I am going to tell you is difficult for me to admit and even harder for me to tell anyone else about. Sarah, I was recently diagnosed with breast cancer, and after a treatment last week, I had bouts of nausea, and was feeling sick most of the time. I was unable to concentrate fully on the report you asked me to complete." Her eyes filled with tears and Sarah reached out to hold her hand. She knew her job was to listen and not come up with some quick response. "I appreciated very much that you cared enough to see me yesterday. The fears I had about telling you about my present diagnosis just melted away. I am so grateful you took the initiative."

The treatment made it difficult for Maria to concentrate on her job. It was even more difficult for her to let Sarah know about it until now. Sarah's intuition of caring was rewarded in trusting her concern for Maria. Unscientific faith is a person's ability to integrate business acumen with compassion. Sarah and Maria worked out a program and gave her additional support, besides her own moral support. Maria recovered and is a trusted associate, as is Sarah who learned the importance of showing a compassionate face and a new leadership skill. Who was the coach? They both were to each other.

Practical Applications for Caregivers

In a previous chapter, I gave a definition of who are caregivers? Do you recall? "Who are caregivers," I asked, and then responded, "We all are in one way or another." I have come to believe caregiving is at the heart of being human. Each of us has developed skills through hours of training, skills that are necessary to our particular profession or calling. Skills that demand analytic thought, logic, use of language, the logos of a situation. All are functions of the left side of the brain. I don't want a bicycle repairman taking out my appendix, nor an untrained paramedic extracting me out of my overturned car. When I arrive in the emergency room on a stretcher, my expectation is that I will receive competent and exceptional care from a group of highly trained healthcare professionals. Linear thinking, linear skills, linear measurements that help in making a diagnosis. Faithless science at its best. As important as training and skills are, patient satisfaction scores consistently show that taking an extra moment to show concern and compassion, of actively listening and demonstrating people skills are what most surveys rank as exceptional care. A lack of these concerns ranks lower as ordinary care or even bad care.

Angels to the Rescue

I am grateful for the emergency care I received after my car turned over on its side while on my way to a coaching session. Their skills were integrated with a real concern for me. I vividly remember telling myself to slow down and bear to the right as I traveling up a winding "S" curve road cut through a hill. I remembered from other experiences cars barreling down the hill from the other direction. Then, all I remember was a kaleidoscope of a canopy of trees and rocks entering my consciousness. Multicolored linear images of rows of weather-aged rocks and huge brown and blacked branches of green leaves of California silver oaks spinning. Apparently, as I was bearing to the right, my right fender hit the lower portion of the hill in such a way that the car just flipped on its side. Perfect physics! As is true with most traumas, what is called trauma amnesia, I blacked out.

Lying on my side with my seat belt intact, I was woken up by someone dressed in white (could it have been my guardian angel?) knocking on the window and telling me to turn off my motor. Like waking up from a stupor, sort of stunned, I said to myself, "Well this is a strange situation!" I reached for the button on the dashboard, turned off the motor, and then loosened my seat belt. Without my knowing it, a first responder climbed up and opened the passenger side door and asked if she could help me get out. I vaguely remember a hand reaching out to me as I stood up. I have no recollection getting out of the car.

A paramedic came over to examine me and encouraged me to go to the hospital to rule out a possible concussion. He, while skillful, was kind and concerned about how I was doing. His compassion is what I remember. It was more than a job to him and his people skills were top notch. No time to tell him I used to do customer service for different hospitals in my prior employment. Sirens blaring, IV running, taking a blood smear to see if I was diabetic, I don't remember much more on the six-mile run to the hospital. Before I knew it, I was wheeled into an emergency room cubicle accompanied by the paramedics and an ER nurse. She was welcoming and reassuring, as later I would learn they were concerned that I may have had a concussion. With some blood work, a trip to the x-ray department, and a thorough exam by the attending physician, I was good as new.

When I recounted the events of the accident to the hospital staff, they were all surprised that I was not more seriously injured. In fact, when the results of the head x-rays returned, they were negative. I remember joking, "What did you expect, there was nothing up there anyway." Again, I was impressed with their kindness and professionalism. Here was unscientific faith, where kindness and a real compassion, real people skills, were practiced. While following their protocols, their care was exceptional. I was admitted for observation and released the next day. I had to leave. I had tickets to see "Madame Butterfly." In retrospect, I am very fortunate. The accident could have been tragic. Hit by an oncoming car, or even the car starting on fire could have been my demise. While wearing a seatbelt was surely a factor in not getting seriously injured, I want to also believe in those angels who saved me.

Too Busy to Care

One of the biggest complaints that patients have when going to the emergency room, is the lack of people skills that some emergency healthcare professionals have. Often this is caused by the triage system most emergency departments use to distinguish the most critical and life-threatening patients from those with less emergent needs. Often emergency rooms become the public health agency of the city or county, as doctor's offices are closed, and urgent care centers are not available in a particular service area. Too much is asked of these dedicated professionals who have to wrestle with priorities. Most of the time they get it right, as they did for me. The following is a case where they didn't.

Sally was working with her husband on a remodel of her kitchen. As they were tearing apart some cabinets, she slipped and stepped on one of the rusty nails sticking out from one of the torn studs. It was a Saturday afternoon, and Sally became concerned about what to do. Remembering a friend who had to get a precautionary tetanus shot for a similar accident, she decided to search the web for answers. She discovered that a tetanus shot had to be given within a certain time after the accident.

Realizing that Monday would be too late to wait to see her doctor and knowing what the complications of not getting a shot could lead to, Sally decided it was best to go to the ER to alleviate her fears. Unfortunately, it was a busy night. The triage nurse took the information and since her situation was not emergent, she told Sally, that, she would have a long wait. It was monotoned, matter of fact information with little empathy for what Sally was feeling. Non-emergent, Sally thought to herself, "But it is, I don't want to risk the complications of not getting the shot." Each had a different view of what emergent meant.

On the one hand, the nurse was correct, Sally was not having a stroke, bleeding to death, or having a heart attack in her view, this could have been handled at an urgent care center. Yes, but they were closed. On the other hand, the nurse could have acknowledged the seriousness of the situation, calmed any fears Sally had, and reassured her that she would do her best to make the wait as short as possible. For Sally, this was an emergent situation, otherwise she would not have come to the ER. The task of the triage nurse was to evaluate the seriousness of the situation and decide when Sally could see the doctor. Job done, logic and left brain to be awarded. Yet, with a little more empathy, the situation could have been much better, as discussed above. Instead of being calm, Sally began to fume, because of how the nurse treated her. Crusty and proficient to the core, she thought.

The two-hour wait seemed like eternity, and it could have been much different. When a survey arrived in the mail about her experience in the ER, she gave them a low score.[41] Needless to say, administration was not pleased as the ER scores were declining. An action plan was put into place where a fast track was developed within the ER.

Suck it up, Baby, Twist, and Shout

My experience as a healthcare professional has taught me that most caregivers face a particular dilemma. They go from call to call, case to case, meeting one need after another. Especially in emergent situations, they tend to "stuff" their feelings or "suck" it up because they must move on to the next call, the next incident, the next whatever. They enter what I call *"the dance of caregiving."* Caregivers built walls to protect themselves, and yet, these same walls often separate and can distance them from those they are called to serve. These walls also prevent the caregiver from listening to those interior movements seeking attention, as well as doing the necessary debriefing on what is being felt.

Normal Feelings

Caregivers often forget that because of who they are and their unique calling to service, they are going to feel what is going on and that these feelings are legitimate and even noteworthy. Contrary to a perception among caregivers that they have to protect themselves from their emotions, be tough and rough it out, caregivers are human with the same emotions and feelings as everyone else. I have come to believe this is the reason they shut down. What is being felt in a traumatic event is a normal reaction to an abnormal situation. There is an interplay at work between faithless science and unscientific faith, between protection (the left-brain function) and creativity (the right brain function). Protection is a function to survive where logical, rational, linear, sequential, concrete processing, take priority. The creative, institutive, compassionate, non-verbal, symbolic, random, and holistic processing often takes a secondary role, that seeks different alternatives. The miracle is that these functions are integrated actions of both the left and right hemispheres of the brain.

I Felt Alone

Allison is a member of EMS (Emergency Medical Service) who was called to the crash of a twin-engine plane where the pilot was trapped. The pilot had radioed that he was having engine trouble before the crash. By the time she and her team arrived, the plane was engulfed in flames. Flashing red and yellow lights against the background of billowing plumes of gray cindered smoke, the smell of gasoline, and orange flames spewing towards the sky greeted the EMS team. Firefighters sprayed foam that resembled a washing machine overflowing and going awry. But it was too late, too hot, too dangerous to make an attempt to save the pilot. The cockpit was already filled with flames.

Every fiber of her body tightened as Allison witnessed what seemed to be impossible. Fight or flight responses at a standstill, caught in the liminal space of non-action. Skills, training, hours of preparation, could not have changed the situation. Their training taught them not to put their own lives at risk when any action they could have taken would be futile. "I just stood there, fixated and almost frozen" Allison recalls, "standing there in horror and staring at him in the flames. He was still in a seated position like he was driving a car. I stared and stared, it was all I could do. And all of a sudden, he took his last breath, his body slowly fell forward and rested on the controls," Allison, with tears in her eyes said that all they could do was watch the pilot hunch over and die. They could do nothing. Frozen in the moment of horror and hopelessness. "We are trained to do all that is possible to save lives and here for a moment that seemed like hours, we stood paralyzed in our inability to do anything."

Because they cared, each member of the team felt hopeless, stunned, and numb. What if they arrived earlier? What if the plane didn't explode? What if the pilot was less injured upon impact and could get out? Again, normal reactions to an abnormal traumatic event. Allison still recalls the face of a firefighter walking around like a zombie. He was pale and sweaty, and no one could talk to him. He was just gone. No one could do anything. Feelings, she admitted, were stirring within her. Feelings Allison would later admit were fear, guilt, grief, and hopelessness. Allison didn't recognize at first, the impact this event would have on her. Her emotions had shut down. Traumatic amnesia is a wonderful gift, as Allison did not remember much about the incident for a week or so. Then she told me that she was moody, even bitchy, and didn't sleep well. She snapped at the smallest things and didn't understand why. She would cry at the drop of a hat and screamed at her fiancé when he suggested that he wanted to take flying lessons.

A First Responder's Dilemma

The commander set up a voluntary debriefing for the team according to the ICISF protocols.[42] Reluctantly, Allison decided to attend, fighting the decision up to the day of the meeting, "Why the hell do I need this?" While not remembering all the details of the debriefing, she recalled that all the members of her team were experiencing the same reactions that she was. "I wasn't crazy, and I felt not so alone."

Allison felt such a sigh of relief. Her team members were moody, drinking heavily, and not sleeping, experiencing emotions just as she was.

As first responders, Allison, like her teammates, when asked "How are you doing?" would answer "Fine, Just Fine," a first responder's code with a double meaning: The first means keep your distance because I am not going to get involved with debriefing and join what was commonly known as the "Cry Babies Club." A real conundrum, being strong at all costs, able to handle the situation by one's self, stuck in the cultural milieu of "I can handle this," and the real experience of being vulnerable. Allison mentioned that first responders often use the anagram F.I.N.E to disguise what they are really feeling. F.I.N.E. means "FUCKED UP, INSECURE, NEEDY, and EMOTIONAL."

Allison knew she really needed help. Having stuffed her feelings, and for whatever reasons, now she was ready to seek help. She knew that the other alternative would be a slow burn to self-destruction. This traumatic event shook her and the team to the core of their being. It left them all speechless and in shock because they experienced normal reactions to an abnormal, traumatic, and horrific event. I simply cannot imagine how I would cope with a similar situation. The symptoms of PTSD were setting in, which often occur within 72 hours after experiencing a traumatic event. It would take Alison years to recognize she was suffering from post-traumatic stress and then do something about it.

Conclusion

One of the requirements for my MA in counseling psychology was to have a personal therapist during the two-year program, as well as a supervisor in my practice hours of counseling. Research had shown, that while one is learning theory, at the same time, during the practice of counseling, personal issues would and could emerge where one needed a resource for debriefing and self-reflection. It was not an option. This was a degree requirement. Not an either/or, but a both/and where the activities of the left and right hemispheres of the brain worked together.[42] As discussed, there are a lot of "what ifs" after a traumatic event. What if these "what ifs" were a way that could be turned around to develop a new paradigm shift within the organization.

What if caregivers had a similar requirement during their training? That is, the recognition that they were going to experience normal reactions to abnormal traumatic situations. Instead of considering debriefing in what some would call "The Crybabies Club," or that one is not strong enough. What if debriefing was the normal routine instead of being hit and miss? Surely the outcome would be a stronger support team that not only had each other's back, but also normalized the human need for reflection and support. Would this not also increase employee satisfaction, decrease turnover, and sick days? I am reminded of an example I used in employee orientation. I had great fun using a commercial from the California Milk Advisory Board that always gives me a chuckle. The focus is that happy employees increase client satisfaction, as well as reduce complaints, and empower the customers that they serve. While it is about cows and cheese, the metaphor is obvious. "Great cheese comes from happy cows. Happy Cows come from California. Real California Cheese."[43] Happy caregivers and happy clients!

What if caregivers were given the opportunity that "the new normal" would be a more effective way of developing emotional intelligence, instead of the bias that debriefing is secret, abnormal, or a club for crybabies? Would there be more empowerment and better relationships with each other and their supervisors? Would there be less of a willingness just to "hold on" until retirement, and most importantly, less fear that one could develop compassion fatigue, burnout, or compound PTSD. Finally, studies have shown that happy employees increase client satisfaction, reduce turnover, and lower costs.[44]

Caregivers often experience the angst of wishing to improve their skills and wanting to be better both personally and professionally. Often one feels stuck, so to say, overwhelmed with too many choices that leads one to confusion and non-action. Often the fear of change or the unknown of what one would experience or feel appears to be more painful and fearful than opening the door. Caregivers often dull their interior pain, and paint, as I like to call it, the bars of their cells gold. As did Allison. The person she was becoming frightened her more than taking the risk to open the door of the jail cell that the traumatic event created. Understanding this process of being present to both inner and outer resources is the subject of our next chapter, Chapter Five: *The Ins and Outs of Hospitality* in which we focus on the interior attitude of hospitality.

Timeout: A Moment of Reprieve

At your own pace, give yourself a moment of leisure to reflect on each question below.

1. While we are a combination of the different functions of the brain, what is your most prominent function, and how does this affect your work as a caregiver?

2. Which of the different stories can you most identify with?

3. What practical suggestions and goals could you make for better self-care for yourself and your colleagues?

4. What do you find difficult about having opportunities for debriefing from traumatic situations?

Chapter 5 - The Ins and Outs of Hospitality

Introduction

The ins and outs of hospitality involves an exploration of creating both inner and outer space, conscious and unconscious musings like breathing in and breathing out. Interior musings alert one to practice the acts of hospitality, an ancient word which means both host and guest reaching outward to the stranger. Ancient cultures well understood the importance of being host to the stranger, as in many cases it meant the very survival of the guest. This was the norm in many societies that outlined the responsibilities for both host and guest. Protected by the host, the guest was treated with respect, fed, sheltered, and considered temporarily, a part of the tribe or clan. The host and guest were equals.

A Universal Understanding of Hospitality

In ancient Greece, hospitality was a right, and the host was expected to make sure the needs of the guest were met. A person's ability to abide by the laws of hospitality determined nobility and social standing.[45] The Sanskrit adage, "Atithi Devo Bhava," meaning the guest is truly your god, dictates the respect granted to guests in India. From a Hindu perspective, the practice of graciousness towards a guest comes from the belief that the guest was either favored by the gods or was a god themselves, and in offering hospitality, the host would find favor.[46] The Hebrew Scriptures recall the stories of hospitality when Abraham becomes the host to three visitors (Genesis 18:1ff), and Lot and his wife offer hospitality to two strangers (Genesis 19:1ff). Noteworthy is how universal, if not archetypal, the theme of hospitality is emerging in the history of humankind. The guests of Abraham and Lot are angels, representing the sacred, the divine God. At the beginning of the Common Era, the Roman poet Ovid retells a Greek myth about Baucus and Philemon who are hosts to two gods, Jupiter and Mercury who are disguised as humans.[47] Their names would be Zeus and Hermes according to the Greek pantheon of gods.

Both the stories in Genesis and Metamorphoses tell us Baucus and Philemon and Lot and his wife are favored because of they offered hospitality, unlike the parsimonious citizens who rejected their need for shelter and safety. Each story tells how they were welcomed, offered the customs of hospitality, the ritual custom of foot washing, of being fed with a meal reserved for honored guests, and given shelter. Because of their generosity and graciousness, Baucus and Philemon, and Lot and his wife were blessed and saved from the destruction of their towns, because the other residents refused to grant hospitality to the strangers.

In early Christianity, it was a common belief that in welcoming a stranger, you may be welcoming a god. By practicing hospitality in welcoming the stranger, you would be blessed. This practice is both praised and enumerated among the works of charity by which humankind will be judged. Matthew speaks about the rewards of the just, related to the Son of Man: "I was a stranger and you welcomed me." (Mat.25:35ff). Jesus had no home and was frequently a guest as is mentioned throughout the Christian Scriptures.[48] Recall the story of Jesus rebuking Simon, his host, because he did not offer Jesus the customary rituals of hospitality, even in preparation for his death. These rituals were the obligation of Simon, to wash Jesus' feet, and offer him the customary welcome for a guest.[49] When Paul and Barnabas were ministering to the citizens of Lystra, the crowds shouted "The gods have come down to us in human form"[50] and later in Jerusalem, Paul exhorts the Hebrew community: "Do not neglect to show hospitality to strangers, for by doing that, some have entertained angels without knowing it."[51]

Archetypal Underpinnings of Hospitality

I want to explore this ancient belief that when the host offers hospitality to a stranger, he may be entertaining an angel or a god. This insight is central to our discussion, and it is the belief of this author, that our experience as caregivers is transformational and is a sacred work. In our numerous acts of hospitality, of creating inner space to welcome the stranger, we, as caregivers, are given opportunities to ignite that sacred spark of life within us. We meet the sacred in the other and in doing so, discover the sacred in ourselves. William Augsburger discusses this interplay between the caregiver and the one being cared for, which I believe, is another fundamental attitude for the host. When the host is sensitive to the needs or wounds of the stranger, there is an interplay, a building of trust, and the experience of compassion. Likewise, as the host becomes an agent of healing, "when healing calls to healing," there is awareness, insight, repentance, change, as well as growth, and h/she is transformed."[52]

This interplay has a way of moving us out of ourselves and into our common humanity. Understanding the practicalities of being a host is paramount to being a caregiver. Caregivers are hypervigilant 24/7, in responding to the call to offer hospitality to those in need. Caregivers practice hospitality par excellence each time they create the space to welcome a stranger. So universal is this act of hospitality, that during times of need and during national emergencies or responses to floods, hurricanes, and fires, first responders and volunteers act without hesitation, responding to the stranger in danger. Even those affected reach out to their neighbors to offer support and safety. As host, being hospitable is about welcoming, being open and receptive, an action that is focused toward another, as in welcoming a guest or a stranger.

Whether a stranger appears in the emergency room, or at the scene of a crime, or at a burning home or building, or to meet the changing needs of an elderly or sick family member, caregivers, by their act of caregiving, train to be hospitable. "Hospitality holds the promise of sharing the best of what we have."[53] Giving the best also demands a discipline that, at times, is challenged and strained. How often one hears that the client or patient comes first, and the client and patient are always right, even if they are wrong. This attitude raises a multitude of conflicting feelings. How does a caregiver cope with difficult and painful situations? How often does the situation challenge the core of our beliefs? Such was the experience of Allison in the previous chapter. Charles, a chaplain at a large medical center, gives us another example of how he discovered one way he was able to sort out his own feelings in a tragic situation. Chaplains too, need time to debrief. Here is his story.

Grandpa, I Can't Play Football

Young Guillermo lay in a coma on a ventilator in the intensive care unit as the doctor called a family conference to discuss the child's dire prognosis and plan of care. Gathered in the ICU conference room were the chaplain, Charles, a social worker, Guillermo's doctor, and his parents, Anita and Billy. Also present was the child's grandfather, Sergio. Sergio spoke of all the dreams he had for Guillermo and how proud he was to be his grandfather. Guillermo was adventurous as any two-year-old, interested in outdoors and loved to be in the family pool with his parents. This summer day, his mother was busy with some friends and relatives planning Guillermo's second birthday party. One of the cousins was charged to keep an eye on Guillermo. Somehow, he wandered into the kitchen and saw the water of the pool glimmering through the locked screen door. He wanted to go swimming and determined as any two-year-old can be, he jumped up and unhinged the lock on the door.

Meanwhile, laughs and giggles over the coming birthday party could be heard in the living room. Distracted by a visitor at the door, no one noticed the absence of Guillermo. Then a cry, "Where is Guillermo?" They searched the rest of the house to no avail, even looking under the bed where Guillermo often would hide, but he couldn't be found. Then they noticed the latch on the kitchen door was unhinged and terrified they searched the yard, discovering Guillermo lying on the bottom of the pool. The paramedics could not find a heartbeat but struggled to revive him. He was medivacked to the hospital by helicopter with a faint brainwave.

Since Guillermo was found without a heartbeat, and he was underwater for at least thirty minutes, it was doubtful he could survive. However, children often do survive, but he sustained severe brain damage. The family agreed to continue treatment and hope for the best. Each member of the support team personally felt the tragedy of this family, especially those with children. The next day, the chaplain held a debriefing at the patient-care rounds with the staff. When it was his turn to share his experiences, Charles explained that he is able to sort out his own feelings by writing in his journal. He found that writing and sorting out the emotions he felt, often helped him debrief in recognizing a situation that was too difficult to bear. As he wrote, a poem emerged which he shared called "Grandpa, I can't play football anymore." Here is his poem:

Each time Guillermo's eye caught the reflection of glimmering light, he ran for the pool. Young, energetic, he was always stopped by a guardian who knew the danger of a two-year-old toddler falling into a swimming pool.

Doors locked, watchful eyes, careful to harness the energy of Guillermo who forgot he could not live in water.

Careful each moment, except one moment that changed everything. All the dreams, all the hopes, all the wishes of a family changed that afternoon when Guillermo thought he was a fish.

A visitor to the door, a mix-up in who was watching a curious thunderbolt, and thunderbolt he did, out the door and into the pool. Thirty minutes he laid there, on the bottom. Life being pushed out of him by the displacement of air for water.

"Where's Guillermo?" The scream of a mother and family members. 911 and drugs and CPR as dedicated first responders cannot change that moment.

His grandfather sighs, his dreams lost for his only male grandson who lives only minimally, whose loss of oxygen leaves him in a deep coma.

In the silence, in the unspoken words and unfocused look, he thinks he hears a voice: "Grandfather, I can't play football anymore."

The Different Faces of Hospitality

Creating space for the other allows the host also to entertain a curiosity about the client's story, a willingness to be receptive to their fears, anxieties, and concerns. This second dimension of hospitality deals with the caregiver's skill and practice of active listening in further understanding the stranger's needs. I remember listening attentively while one of my professors addressed the importance of active listening during one of my courses in pastoral counseling. She said there are three rules that are the foundation of a great coach, caregiver, or counselor. The first rule she said, "is to listen." The second rule she said, "is to listen." Then she paused, allowing silence to activate the class' curiosity, as she regained a quizzical poise, looking somewhat whimsical and a little mischievous as she gazed at each member of the class. She said, "Can you guess what the third rule is in developing the skill of active listening? It is to Listen!"

While there are a variety of definitions for active listening, I like the one posted for diplomats on the U.S. Department of State website. This gives the inquirer a visual metaphor that symbolizes the act of listening. The Chinese character tells us that to listen we must use both ears, watch and maintain eye contact, give undivided attention, and finally, to be empathetic. The article further states that there are four rules to active listening that help explain the deeper meaning of the Chinese symbol. These are: to seek to understand before you seek to be understood, to be non-judgmental, to give the individual your undivided attention, and to use silence effectively.54

While much about hospitality is given to creating space for others, little attention is given to the inner promptings that the act of hospitality stirs within the caregiver. Promptings and feelings can both increase and deplete one's energies. The third understanding of hospitality focuses on the interior stirrings of the caregiver. Simply put, what does the caregiver experience, and how does h/she address these insights and a pantheon of feelings? These can range from feelings of endearment, excitement, satisfaction, and joy over a job well done, to feelings of vigilance, caution, suspicion, hopelessness, anxiety, fear, and compassion fatigue. Simultaneously, hospitality is about another, and at the same time, listening to the interior promptings of one's own Soul. In summary, the three dimensions of hospitality are responding to a need, understanding what the client is experiencing and understanding how you as a caregiver are affected. Inner and outer space seem to merge whether one begins with the need of another or with one's own self.

Lost in Reverie

My earliest understanding of hospitality surprised me, the summer I turned thirteen. In hindsight, I found myself being host to the stranger within me that I had often neglected. I was too young and inexperienced to fully understand these interior promptings of my Soul. They were strange to me. I was sitting on a hill overlooking a railroad track. The abandoned track seemed to meander through the edge of town, and I was curious as to when the last train passed through. I also tried to imagine where it was going and where it came from. I loved trains and had a large layout on two 4' x 8' sheets of green painted plywood in the attic with trestles, roads, houses, and a tunnel through a paper mache mountain.

I am not sure how I wandered off from my brother and father, who together were on an errand to get our car serviced. My father's friend owned an auto repair shop just in front of the railroad tracks. Car talk was not my interest, and since there would be an hour or so for the car to be serviced, I was left to my own devices. We toured the shop and then we were on our own. Maybe I said, "Dad, I am going for a walk." I was content, wandering behind the garage and going up this hill. I found a grassy spot overlooking the tracks, and I imagined I was sitting on a trestle with my feet dangling in the air. In many ways, I entered a threshold between what was before and what would happen next, an in-between place. Varying shades of gravel created a bed that cushioned the creosote-covered railroad ties, ties that fastened and held the rusted colored tracks. What drew me there, I do not know. I can only speculate. Maybe it was my love of trains or was it the wanderlust of travel, moving beyond a geographical boundary springing from the depths of my ancestral and immigrant past? Maybe it was simply an opportunity just to be, a moment of reverie, a common teenage escape, so to speak.

I was focused on outer space, the warmth of the summer day, the freshness of the grass, wildflowers covering the hill, and the blossoming of new foliage on the nearby grounds. My attention was also on the tracks leading to nowhere, or was it somewhere that I wished I could go? Focused on the railroad tracks, and like a mantra that leads one to interior space, without warning, I was lost in a moment of wonder and reverie. It was as if I had been transported to an inner world of wonder and peace. Time vanished, and for this moment, I felt like I touched infinity. Even as I write, the experience continues to deepen within me, a feeling of transcendence and oneness. For the first time in my life, I experienced Soul when time ceased to exist, I was simply present in the here and now. With this juxtaposition of outer space to inner space and this communion, the two became one. I was too young, however, to glean wisdom from this experience and to understand the stirrings of my Soul. It would take years for me to fathom the depths of this new awareness. After all, I had my turbulent teenage years before me, during which I struggled to understand my place in the world. Those years led me to discover my calling as a caregiver.

Inner and Outer Worlds

I was very much in touch with my surroundings on that spring day. I cannot say I was in touch with my inner world and how to relate it to the rest of my life. In exploring inner and outer worlds, where does one begin? Caregivers are drawn to respond to those in need. Trained as it were, to be self-sufficient, almost on autopilot, walking a tightrope between each of these two worlds. The worlds of a doctor, nurse, caregiver, firefighter, police officer, paramedic, parent, and educator transcend any one participant. Their struggle is humankind's struggle in developing a relationship to interior and exterior resources that reveals something of the mystery of being human.

Inner and outer worlds create inner and outer space, an openness to receive the stranger, an openness to the universe, an openness to the movements of one's Soul, and a receptivity to the story and experience of the stranger. *"Hospitality is a word overflowing with abundance, like the pomegranate, a rich and ruby fruit from the desert, to comfort and delight."*[55] Pomegranates, like some of us caregivers, are crusty and hard on the outside, then in due season when the time is right, we are open, vulnerable and reveal our inner secrets. Pomegranates are a metaphor for self-giving, an ancient symbol of fertility and charity, giving of themselves completely. *As the pomegranate reveals its inner secrets in due season, so too, does Soul refresh with wisdom and insight*, a tagline that I now use in this book. When we become aware and listen, Soul does refresh us with wisdom and insight.

This is the paradox of exploring inner and outer space. Outer leads to the inner and inner leads to the outer. The task for the caregiver is learning that the core of hospitality begins with one's self in the "in between space" where inner and outer worlds meet, that I call the betwixt and between of liminal space. Paraphrasing the words of Psalm 139 from the Hebrew Bible, if we go to the highest heavens, or descend to the netherworld, or take the wings of the morning or dwell in the deepest regions of the sea or think we can hide in the shadows of the night, still that sacred spark of life, that unity of who we are, where inner and outer space meet, will be with and in us."[56]

The mythologist, Joseph Campbell, expands this notion of integrating inner and outer worlds in a discussion he had with one of his students. Campbell was exploring the ancient myths and religious traditions of monotheism and polytheism when one of his students asked: "Where does God live?" Think for a moment what you learned from your parents and religious teachers. Is God in the heavens, in creation, in one another, in your imagination, in your heart? Campbell, somewhat amused, comments: "Is it above? Then the birds will be there before you. Is it below? Then the fish will be there before you. The Kingdom of God is within you. Who and what is in Heaven? God is in Heaven. Where is God? Within you!"[57]

Experience as Teacher

My experience and awareness of hospitality became real for me and matured when I joined a community of Brothers who took a vow of hospitality. For over five hundred years, the Hospitaller Brothers of St.

John of God developed monastery hospitals, clinics, and health centers for the sick and infirm.[58] The focus was outward, creating a space for another which prompted this outer response to host the stranger. In practical terms, the Brothers created monastery hospitals, taking the sick and infirm into their homes, and into their very lives. The brothers became the host to the stranger. I became intrigued how hospitality was lived out in such practical and concrete ways. What was it about hospitality that created this interior attitude of receptivity, and how did it become a spiritual practice?

I had the opportunity to explore this question more deeply while I was attending a post-graduate program at the University of St. Louis. One of the requirements for a pastoral counseling and spiritual direction program I attended, was to do a study of the charism of the religious institute to which I belonged. Charisms are spiritual gifts, special graces that are freely given by a benevolent God to humankind.[59] We can see how these are shown in the lives of such charismatic leaders like Gandhi, Martin Luther King, St. Francis of Assisi, John of God, and Mother Theresa of Calcutta, to name a few. In my research for a deeper understanding of the charism of hospitality, I discovered that the actual practice, experience, and reflection of hospitality was the spiritual foundation of the Order. It wasn't about all the external manifestations of following a specific rule, specific customs for the host, what one wore, or the religious rituals and customs that were added on through the centuries. Hospitality was the actual doing and then the reflection on the specific acts of hospitality that was the core spiritual practice of the Order. All the brothers, no matter their role, each morning would go to the wards and minister to the patients. This reflection added insight and wisdom that created a spirituality and an interior attitude of hospitality. Not something outside of one's action, but rather integral to its practice.

Caregivers and Hospitality

Caregivers practice hospitality every day. Their scope of practice demands an openness that, at a drop of a hat when a call comes in, they are ready to respond. They don't have time for a bad hair day or to deal with their family or personal issues when called to an accident, a bank robbery, a wildfire, or to the side of a critical-care patient. Each response demands attentiveness, and each response affects the caregiver differently because they care. While emotions may be held in check, emotions are there needing to be explored and even understood. Hospitality is directed toward another and at the same time directed toward the caregiver.

Learning to respond to the needs of others is easy for caregivers. Learning to welcome the stirring of emotions of one's Soul is more complicated. Not only is the experience of caregiving often missed, but also the opportunity to be supported, fed, and nourished by the very act of caregiving is often neglected. The experience of reaching out as a caregiver to one who is ill, or in need, or in danger is one of the mysteries of the universe, argues the anthropologist, Dr. Angeles Arrien. She suggests that the caregiver's experience of responding to one who is ill or in need "is an initiation to coming home again to a deeper sense of self and well-being."[60] Listen to the meaning of Dr. Angeles' words, the act of responding, the act of creating space for another, the act of self-sacrificing for another, is a way of finding one's self. While she focuses on the response to illness, I believe a broader understanding can be applied to all the different acts of caregiving. Wholeness and a renewed understanding of one's self seem to be borne out of the trials and experience of hospitality.

Yet, what is the foundation of this interior attitude, which I believe is a spiritual practice? The act of hospitality is rooted in one's interior stirrings of the Soul. It is one thing to believe being a caregiver is my job. It is quite another to believe caregiving is my calling. Years at the bedside as a registered nurse, pastoral counselor, and executive leader, would lead me to a deeper understanding of hospitality. Was I willing to be hospitable not only to those I was called to serve, but more importantly, was I willing to become aware of welcoming those interior movements of my Soul?

Explore with me how the three dimensions of hospitality affected me during one of my routine visits in welcoming a new patient into the hospital. Peter and his family taught me to listen not only to him and to his family, but also to listen to my own inner stirrings.

Untangling the Cords that Bind Us

As I started to knock on Peter's door, I remembered the words of Dr. Christina Puchalski, a dear friend and colleague: "When you knock on the door of a patient, take a deep breath and know *why* you are entering the room."[61] Knocking on the door became a reminder for me to stop, and create that interior space of welcoming, so that I could be receptive to Peter's story. Peter was admitted suffering from pneumonia and inflammation of his lungs, which is a complication and one of the last stages of AIDS. I was the Catholic chaplain on duty that evening.

After introductions, I asked if I could sit on the chair next to his bed. As we spoke, his eyes welled up with tears as he said to me: "You don't know how long I have waited for someone like you to come and visit me." There was no time to dismiss the compliment, which caregivers often do, or to have visions of grandiosity. I had to understand what was meant by his words, what was Peter really trying to say? Although he felt estranged from his church as a gay Catholic, there was still a deep desire within him to feel he belonged and could find reconciliation.

Peter came from a large Catholic Italian family who, as a gay man, tried to reconcile his beliefs with his family and Church. He also knew that he was dying and was seeking comfort and support. He asked for the sacraments. Tears ran down his face as he discovered a deep peace and was grateful that someone understood. Important in itself, as he did not feel so isolated, but also important because he and his partner were coping with their decision not to inform his parents that he was sick or in the hospital. I knew I would have to explore this with him and his parents sooner than later. He asked if I could help, and I reassured Peter that I would in any way I could. I told him I would check on him in the morning, but if he wanted me to come earlier, just call the hospital operator and have me paged. He reached out to hug me. We embraced and said good night.

Paged to Go to My Office

No sooner had I begun my rounds the next day, I got a call that Peter's father, Antonio, was waiting for me in the chaplain's office. He wanted to know if his son was in the hospital. This was the first of three hospitals he intended to visit. Listening to his concerns and fears about his son helped me to understand more about Peter and his father. While understanding the importance of confidentiality and the patient's wishes not to let his family know he was in the hospital, I reassured Antonio that I would investigate and get back to him. Soon after, I visited Peter. "Peter, your dad was here earlier and wanted to visit you." Peter began to cry. "Yes, I do want him to come; I want to tell him what is wrong with me. Can you help me?" Peter expressed to me his fears and inability to face his family by himself in the past, and even more so today, due to his weakened condition. He just couldn't bear the possibility of being rejected. I asked if I could have his permission to call his family to come visit and tell them his diagnosis. That afternoon, his dad, Antonio, and mother, Lucia came with two of Peter's four brothers, Markus and Georgio. We met in the chaplain's office.

I remember leading them down the hall as I felt the intrigue building up. I wanted to be understanding and receptive to the needs of Peter's parents. They, too, were affected by Peter's illness. They, too, were strangers needing a safe harbor. I had no idea what the outcome of this meeting would be, but I realized it's importance. All I could do was to create a space of welcoming and actively and compassionately listen. I shared with them my initial awkwardness in not informing them of Peter's condition until I had his permission. During the conversation, Antonio asked about his son's condition. "Do you know what is wrong with my son?" There was silence. I waited for some response from one of his brothers with whom Peter had earlier shared his diagnosis, but there none. Just more silence.

Perhaps the silence was due to their awkwardness in discussing AIDS openly with their parents present. After a few minutes that seemed more like ten, I broke the silence explaining that Peter requested I speak to them, as it was too difficult for him. Too many years and opportunities had passed, and too many unspoken words weighed heavily on Peter to tell them himself. I told them of the seriousness of his condition, that his immune system was failing and that his prognosis was poor. You could hear a pin drop, as all were focused on me as I continued, "Antonio and Lucia, your son has AIDS, and he is in the final stages of the disease."

The Sounds of Silence

Surprised and yet not surprised, his mother, Lucia tearfully said this is what she always suspected. Mothers always know. More silence, deliberate silence, as I wanted the silence to permeate their hearts as they searched for answers. They each tried to avoid looking at each other and became more focused on me. I was expecting one of the two brothers to speak up and support their parents. Again silence. Then Antonio, looking up sheepishly, his face etched with emotion, asked poignantly, "What should we do?" I paused for a moment, knowing, so conscious of the fact that many families rejected their gay sons and daughters with AIDS during the height of the epidemic. As I made eye contact with Antonio, the words gently came forward from the deepest resources of my heart. "You need to love him!"

Like an arrow aimed at each of their hearts, the truth of what I said allowed them to feel the pain of their son's diagnosis, as well as to see what each of them needed to do. Tears filled the room and I choked up. Each knew, loving Peter was what each of them wanted and needed to do. "Can we see him?" both Lucia and Antonio seemed to intone at the same time, full of eagerness, full of a parent's love. "Yes, of course, Peter is expecting you." The nurses on the floor, as well as Peter, knew that I was meeting with his family. It seemed the nurses were holding a silent vigil as I escorted the family past the nurses' station and knocked on Peter's door. "Peter," I said, "your parents and brothers want to see you." I vaguely remember what happened next, as I remained on the sidelines as Lucia and Antonio almost smothered Peter with hugs and kisses. Then, his brothers Markus and Georgio, one by one took Peter's hand and hugged him. Peter was beside himself, as there was no need for excuses or explanations. There was not a dry eye in the room nor at the nurse's station. Each nurse on duty also came in to meet Peter's family. In a moment, all the worries and fears of a gay son vanished in the embrace, and he experienced love from his family. The silence of the years was broken as we all deeply felt the numinosity of reconciliation.

It was my privilege to witness their individual fears surrender to a greater collective need to restore the family unity that is such an important a part of their Italian heritage. Peter was no longer a stranger, but a welcomed and restored member of his family. Each day, different members of his family came to visit. When it was time for Peter to transition to Hospice care, they came faithfully each day with food and helped his partner with daily care until Peter died three months later. He died happy, reconciled with and surrounded by his large Italian family. The logjam of silence was finally broken in the honesty and the integrity of the love a father has for his son. Peter's illness became a portal for him and his father to begin a needed conversation, one that might have been lost forever, if not for this experience.

Conclusion

The ins and outs of hospitality lead one on a journey, a pilgrimage of self-awareness and transformation. Following centuries of tradition and custom across different cultural and spiritual practices, hospitality is ingrained in the Soul of caregivers. While being host to a stranger, the act of hospitality demands an internal discipline to be open, to be welcoming, to be receptive to the stranger who knocks on our door. In a paper for my certification to be a Board-Certified Chaplain for the National Association of Catholic Chaplains, I had to present my personal understanding and pastoral approach to my work as a pastoral counselor.[62] I chose to share my reflections on Hospitality that have continued to be a touchstone in being a caregiver. I have come to believe that the heart of compassion is hospitality, and the practice of hospitality is the ability to welcome another. To welcome another means to accept and be present to where the other is, to be present to one's pain, abandonment, faith, crisis, doubts, anger or fears. One can only be present or hospitable and therefore, empathetic and compassionate if one can understand these same experiences within oneself. If the caregiver denies their own anger, grief, loss, pain or suffering, they cannot be hospitable to another.

To be hospitable means to be present in such a way that the one who is in need discovers within themselves the capacity for and the possibility of one's dignity being restored through their encounter with the caregiver. Concurrently, as the caregiver is welcoming the stranger and facilitating this process, h/she rediscovers their own human dignity being restored. This transformation is similar to gods or angels appearing through the acts of hospitality. The ins and outs of hospitality define that special relationship each caregiver experiences and what makes the work we do so rewarding and life-giving. The paradox of this relationship is that the one who wishes to comfort and be a host is also the one who is comforted and transformed.

There is much to develop about this interaction between the caregiver, the one in need and the caregiver's need for self-care. There is also much to explore in what some consider to be a minefield of one's emotional intelligence or lack of support or what hinders one in their service to another. Chapter Six, "Love is a Wounded Healer," will explore in depth the archetype of the wounded healer and how each caregiver can own and resource its life-giving energies.

Timeout: A Moment of Reprieve

At your own pace, give yourself a moment of leisure to reflect on each question below. Be creative. Reflect with a spouse or friend, trusted co-worker, spend time taking a walk, writing in a journal, writing a poem, tending to a garden, listening to music, writing a song, or drawing a picture.

1. What is one of your favorite stories of being a caregiver that continues to give you goosebumps or makes you tear? (I must admit, I was in tears of gratitude as I talked about Peter and his Family).

2. Can you give an example of when you went out of your way to practice the skill of active listening to one of your clients?

3. In exploring the different dimensions of hospitality, what has been your experience in being the host, in being aware of the client's story, and of recognizing your own feelings.

4. What is most difficult for you in allowing yourself to become aware of what has been most painful for you in your service to others?

Hospitality

an ancient word
which means both
host and guest.

Its meaning holds the
promise of sharing
the best of what we have.

It is a word overflowing
with abundance
like the pomegranate —
a rich ruby fruit from the desert
to comfort and
to delight.

Chapter 6 - Love is a Wounded Healer

Introduction

The personal journey of caregivers is a heroic adventure. Heroic, because of all the possibilities of discovering within themselves their values and strengths, as well as a deeper understanding of woundedness. Woundedness implies those interior shadow sides of ourselves that seek wholeness and healing. In the midst of woundedness, sometimes kicking and screaming, sometimes overcome with the pain of what life has given us, or sometimes lost in the cauldron of heated emotions, we are presented with an opportunity to find meaning. The call, the ability, and the skill to respond to the one in need, to enter into a situation that could be fraught with danger, and to be sensitive in responding to woundedness, is, I believe, the same ability and skill to enter into our own woundedness, which is often revealed in our daily tasks of caregiving.

In a culture that demands perfection in all that we do, it is difficult to reconcile that we, as caregivers, skillful and talented as we can be, don't have all the answers and are confronted with our limitations, personal issues, and woundedness. What within us draws us to the woundedness of others? A skill we often underestimate. Another more poignant question that challenges our imagination and curiosity is: What is it within a person, whether caregiver or the one in need that draws each to labor with, endure, and come to terms with woundedness, illness, and traumatic events? A mystery not to be solved, but to be explored. This ability to enter into, to hold, to guide, and to sustain oneself or another through the mystery of being a caregiver is best described as the archetypal image of the wounded healer.

To say that love is a wounded healer is to imply, on the one hand, that caregivers bring to each situation their human capacity to care, to be empathetic, to heal, and create positive outcomes. At the same time, and almost simultaneously, caregivers can be confronted with their limitations, particular boundaries, woundedness, and vulnerabilities that life brings. Herein lies a truth about the paradox of caregiving: a wounded healer responds to one in need, and conversely, the person in need is given the opportunity to be an agent of healing for the caregiver. The very act of caregiving becomes transformational and may lead to the caregiver's personal and professional growth. Now wait a moment, this seems to be backward, but it is not.

Our previous discussion in Chapter Five recalls the insight of William Augsburger who spoke about the unique relationship between caregiver and client.[63] Simply put, it means that when the caregiver is sensitive to his or her own limitations and woundedness, h/she is better able to understand the woundedness of the one in need and to respond with compassion. This leads to a greater awareness, insight, a change of heart and growth. For purposes of our discussion, we are all caregivers in one way or another. As discussed earlier, caregivers are parents who care for their children, adult children that care for their parents, spouses who care for each other, first responders, police, firefighters, emergency, medical responders, healthcare professionals, and educators to name a few.

The archetype of the Wounded Healer conveys the inner reality that within the healer, the person doing the act of caregiving, is woundedness, and within the one wounded, the one seeking care from the caregiver, sleeps a healer. There is a similarity to the Buddhist symbol of the yin and the yang which acknowledges that within darkness there is a spark of light, and within the light, there is a shadow of darkness. The caregiver's sensitivity to the woundedness of the one in need is borne out of his or her self-knowledge and experience of woundedness. Likewise, the healer function within the one seeking care is activated by the sensitivity and compassion of the caregiver.

Guggenbühl-Craig refers to this dynamic as the healer-client function or what we understand as the caregiver and the one in need. He maintains that when a person seeks a caregiver and healer, an intra-psychic or 'inner healer' or 'healing factor' is also energized.[64]

Who is the Healer: The Caregiver or the One in Need?

This interplay between the caregiver and the one in need is a humbling, yet empowering experience. I remember well my internship at an outpatient geriatric psychiatric center for my master's in counseling psychology. I was asked to facilitate a group session of six to eight clients around the theme of relying on their interior or spiritual strengths to cope with their particular mental health issues. I had always believed that a person was more than their presenting diagnosis. The task was to explore if the clients could discover these pockets of gold within themselves that would help them cope with their illness. We began each session by asking a simple question, what did you discover about yourself that carried you through the week, something that brought back happy memories about yourself or about your family or friends?

As each holiday emerged during the year, memories flooded the room. Each person spoke about how remembering helped them cope with their present and lingering crisis. We had fun to such an extent when one day I was leaving the group, the attending psychologist asked me, "What do you do in there? They love you." I smiled and said, "we simply support and validate each other." Now don't get me wrong, we are not holding hands and singing Kumbaya. Yet, we do sing if a client remembers a song, we do affirm when someone discovers a way of coping, and we have learned to communicate and support each other. They gave me more than I feel I gave them.

Knowing the time, we spent together gave the clients an opportunity to discover more about their coping strengths, was in itself, a surprising outcome as they rediscovered joy and made a gradual return to the values that celebrated their lives and helped them cope. They were more than their DSM IV diagnosis.

Rediscovering the Spark of Life

One of the members of the group, Shawn, who was admitted for suicidal ideation, asked to see me privately. He would have been my father's age at the time, in his early sixties. He was a World War II veteran who landed on Normandy beach in France. I didn't realize it then but had later learned that my father was also there on that December day. Raised in an Irish Catholic family, Shawn grew up impoverished, having to wear hand-me-down clothes from his older brothers and shoes whose soles looked like swiss cheese. There were times he and his siblings didn't have enough to eat as money for food was spent mostly on alcohol for his parents. He told me he could not wait to get out of there and join the army. On the eve of D day, being Catholic, he wanted to go to confession realizing the possibility of being killed. He had a secret to tell the priest, and it took all of his courage to say the words that he was gay. Expecting some sort of comfort, the priest called him a dog.

Can you imagine? I cringed over what Shawn said as the pain he carried seemed like a knife plunged into his heart. And here we were, Shawn and I, sitting in the safety of a sunlit conference room in a Catholic hospital, so unlike that dark stormy day of forty years ago, as the waves of the North Atlantic tossed the ship he was on. Despite all of his training, he was just a young soldier as he landed on the sandy beaches of Normandy, not knowing if he would live or die. Thoughts of my father's experience also flooded my consciousness as I began to gain more insight into Shawn's experiences.

Any one of those traumatic experiences could have led him to consider suicide. He was raised in an impoverished alcoholic family that seemed like a war zone, his discovery of being gay, which was against the cultural norms of his day. He suffered undiagnosed primary PTSD from his experience on D day until his discharge, and later in the army, was condemned by a Catholic priest. Any one of these trials could have led to his suicidal ideation.

As we focused on his life story, Shawn began to see he had the inner strength to survive, though he had contemplated suicide. He was able to make the distinction of just wanting to be dead versus wanting to end the emotional and psychic pain that was eating at the core of his being. This awareness led Shawn to embrace his real desire to live. His inner strength for survival now gave him the courage to thrive. Shawn was discharged from the program three months later. He tore up his plan for suicide and joined a local support group. I came as the caregiver, yet it was this group and Shawn who empowered me as a young intern to continue in my role as a counselor. I learned that what I was doing was more than a job, it was my calling.

Who is a Wounded Healer?

Who is a Wounded Healer, and to what extent is the term significant for the caregiver and the one in need? In the broadest sense, we are all wounded healers as being human guarantees that one will experience suffering, limitations, and imperfections. Life has its way, doesn't it? The ancients struggled in a similar way as we do so today, to understand that a person was not a god, but one whose very mortality signified boundaries, imperfections, and woundedness. There are wounds that are emotional, psychological, and spiritual such as depression, alienation, post-traumatic stress, abuse, and lack of meaning in one's life.

A wound may have many meanings such as a physical cut, a broken bone, a contusion, tumor or stroke. A wound implies an injury to a living tissue or the pain experienced by an emotional or psychological injury. Used as a metaphor, woundedness can refer to something as complex as a broken relationship, loss of one's reputation, divorce or loss of a job and in the case of illness, a panorama of physical, emotional, psychological, and spiritual experiences. Some wounds may heal and some may not. While a wound represents a need to heal, the healer function within a person is an attempt to make us whole. Psychoanalysts' Freud and Jung's understanding of woundedness had to do with the process of self-actualization and individuation which was not static in nature, but a dynamic process of gradual growth. Freud and Jung learned insights about psychotherapy from reflection on their own personal suffering and their desire to find meaning and healing.[65] Being human necessitates acknowledgment of weakness, vulnerability, incompleteness, and woundedness.

What Does Woundedness Want?

What does woundedness wish to say to one who is afflicted, experiencing danger or in need? In the depths of the silence, in between the fibers of pain, a voice may be screaming to be heard unraveling from pain's strong arms.[66] One wound, for example, like the loss of a job due to a company's reorganization, may arouse feelings of anger, disappointment, betrayal, and hurt. On the one hand, these are valid experiences. On the other hand, they may resurface deeper feelings of betrayal, of being left out or even forgotten. The wound cries out for attention and healing, not to be denied, avoided, but to be listened to. We caregivers are given the opportunity for self-care by listening to what internally needs to be heard. The wound then becomes a reminder, a voice of a lived experience in the present or in the past. Dennis Slattery seems to sum this up when he writes "wounding is one way the body shows its hyperbole, a way of drawing our attention to it in unexpected ways". [67]

An Unexpected Insight: The Adult Child as Caregiver to a Parent

Annabelle was drawn to woundedness in unexpected ways in becoming the caregiver of her father suffering from Alzheimer's. Miz Annabelle, as she likes to be called, found that as a caregiver to her father, she discovered something about herself that was hidden for years. True to her southern heritage, Annabelle excelled in gracious hospitality, manners, and service. Lordy, she would not have it any other way, as there was a tradition and a family name to uphold. Something we all experience keeping up with the Jones. Raised in Savannah, her mother taught her the fine delicate societal norms of being a Southern Belle, after all her name was Annabelle! To say she loved this role is an understatement. She flaunted it anytime she could, often amusing her father, whom she adored. When her mother died two years earlier, Annabelle assumed the primary caregiver duties.

In the beginning, the obligation to help out became an act of loving service. She had fond memories of their having meaningful conversations. As weeks and months grew into a year and more, her resolve grew thin. "At first," she said, "the obligation led to spending many hours with my dad." This drew her to experience a deeper understanding of compassion, while at the same time, she noticed that her relationship had changed. She was no longer her father's caregiver, but his caretaker. Notice the shift in tone, the shift from two adults communicating equally with each other to one of a parent-child relationship with Annabelle being the parent. Slowly, Annabelle realized that her father was slipping more and more away from her, present in the body, but no longer present mentally, emotionally, or spiritually.

Annabelle was experiencing the first symptoms of anticipatory grief, when one begins to realize something has changed, like the person you love and have known somehow left the room, yet, is still physically present before you. Then one day when asked by her pastor how she was feeling, Annabelle sighed trying to sort out the emotion she felt, like unraveling a string from the ball of yarn she felt buried inside her. "I feel numb," she responded. Yes numb, because she had been burning full throttle on all of her cylinders not realizing she was just worn out using up her reserve energy. Numbness implies a loss of energy, a loss of distinguishing one feeling from another because for so long, she had to stuff her feelings in deference to her father's needs. She was beginning to experience the first signs of burnout. One feeling that did emerge was she often felt guilty. Was she doing enough?

With her pastor's help, Annabelle started questioning, "Am I selfish, if I consider my own needs?" No easy answer as being overwhelmed clouded her judgment. She was consumed in meeting the needs of her father. If she only tried a little harder, spent more time, tried more remedies, would that give her more time with him? Unconsciously, she was trying to fill in a hole that had no bottom, preventing her from experiencing the eventual loss of her father. We caregivers sometimes fail to recognize, as the ancients did before us, we are not gods. Being addicted to perfectionism only becomes self-defeating. The walls of her Southern façade couldn't protect her.

Annabelle pondered. And then she began to question, where does selfishness come from? "Why would I blame myself or feel guilty about meeting my own needs?" she asked. Consider what she discovered in exploring the definition of selfish: inconsiderate, thoughtless, ungenerous, self-indulgent, uncharitable, and self-aggrandizing to name a few.[68] Clearly, this was not the case. If anything, she was selfless, disregarding herself and her own interests. Selfless to such a point, that she silenced the inner promptings of her Soul to care for herself. Important to note that it was only in this place of questioning that Annabelle had come to this juncture. The illness of her father and Annabelle's experience of her own lack of self-care were now her teachers.

Annabelle learned earlier in life that wearing the mask of a Southern Belle, implied that self-care was something softies did. A familiar trap most caregivers fall into. While the relationship changed between Annabelle and her father, he still became the catalyst that brought Annabelle's walls of perfectionism, like the walls of Jericho, come crumbling down. She no longer had to be a steel magnolia, as she was experiencing what a wounded healer is, that gave her permission, now for the first time in her life, to recognize her own vulnerability, her fears, and her limitations and at the same time discover the hidden strengths she had for personal growth and transformation.

Each encounter is an opportunity for both the caregiver and the one receiving care to enter into a healing relationship. Discovering the healer function within the emptiness of one's woundedness is the dynamic of a wounded healer. Carl Jung calls this the process of becoming or individuation.[69] Joseph Campbell believes this process is a mystery to be lived,[70] and James Hillman refers to this dynamic as Soul-making.[71]

Common Through the Ages

Within western philosophy and thought, Plato recognized the importance of the physician as a wounded healer. In *the Republic,* he argued that the most skillful physicians are those who have suffered and learned from a variety of illnesses. Rather than being models of good health alone, they became eloquent examples of the wounded healer. He shares his insights about disease and the need for a physician to understand maladies from his own experience. What Plato recognized about physicians can, I believe, be applied to all caregivers.

Essential in understanding the caregiver as a wounded healer is the belief that those who care for others are themselves wounded. This knowledge not only assists them in their care for others, but also becomes a transformative experience for them. Woundedness implies that each person has wounds that heal and wounds that are always in the process of becoming healed. Individual and collective memories appear and reappear and become enfleshed through the remembrance of the stories. Spirit and flesh agonize with crushing pain as memory attempted to bring to light "bit by bit" what needs to be remembered.[72]

An experience of a traumatic event, such as domestic violence, natural disasters such as wildfires, flooding, earthquakes, combat experiences, physical and sexual abuse, and the different forms of PTSD, post-traumatic stress, are such examples where wounds that one may experience are healed "bit by bit." Memories bring to life both blessings and wounds, and their constant reappearances call out for recognition and awareness. Storytelling and myth help caregivers and those seeking care to put into context the images, memories, feelings, and experiences that activate their imaginations as wounded healers.

Chiron

An example in Greek Mythology of a wounded healer is the divine physician Chiron, the centaur and teacher of the renowned physician Asclepius. The centaurs were creatures with the bodies of horses and with chests, arms, shoulders and heads of men, who descended from Apollo. Mythos attempted to image the reality of a union between spirit and flesh, reason and instinct that are components of each person. Animal, human, and divine instincts are combined in the image of the centaur, Chiron. "He was wise and gentle," comments Christine Downing, and "In this case, his animal nature seemed to signify an attunement to instinctual wisdom and a deep understanding of embodiment, an understanding that informed his gifts as hunter, sculptor, and healer."[73] Chiron is a god who suffers an incurable wound inflicted upon him by a poisoned arrow from Hercules. Is an incurable wound a metaphor to remind us that we are still in a process of becoming? Who of us have reached our full potential as human beings? Sometimes "Soul pain" reminds us of our desire and longing to continue in our process of growth and transformation while at the same time recognizing our limitations and needs, and areas of self-improvement.

Don't you just love the wiggle room this gives us, as caregivers, as being wounded is synonymous with being imperfect, with limitations of the flesh? The fact that Chiron has an incurable wound becomes a metaphor for all of us. In a culture that promotes striving for excellence at a manic pace, it is reassuring to note what we already know intuitively: not everything or everyone is totally perfect or complete. Woundedness is a part of being human. Emotional, physical, psychological, and spiritual suffering may lead one to insight and transformation which springs forth from the depths of our Soul pain.

Wisdom Gleaned from Woundedness

The underlying principle of the mystery of the incurable wound of Chiron that is applicable today appears to be that knowledge is gleaned from our wounds. Descent into the liminal space of one's limitations offers both caregiver and the one in need an opportunity to find meaning and energies of the wounded healer. Caregiver and the one in need each become a transformative agent for the other. The paradigm of the incurable wound of Chiron gives one a unique perspective about being a Wounded Healer that one's wounds is an integral part of being human. So, when we hurt, or experience a traumatic event, or don't understand our struggle in what we are feeling, or just experiencing the numbness of being overwhelmed, instead of beating ourselves up, feeling out of control, or fearful of what is buried within, we can begin to accept and learn from the wonderful gift of being human.

The monster of illness, those fears that may accompany a possible heart attack, did not overcome Bill as he felt a sudden pain and compression in his chest. He had been working excessively hard to meet some deadlines and assumed that what he was feeling had to do with stress. However, the pain did not go away, and the compression became worse. The onset of a possible heart attack brought Bill reluctantly to a different level of consciousness. Independent and self-reliant, acknowledging a crack in the wall he built around him, Bill had to admit he needed help. Giving in to his son's demands, he called 911 and within minutes he was brought to the emergency room, which for Bill was like going to another planet. Since he had never been seriously sick a day in his life, this adventure was certainly not common to him. He was an architect, used to develop plans, and meeting deadlines. This date with illness was not penciled in on his calendar.

The emergency room staff recognized the possibility of a major heart attack and quickly surrounded their patient, who bristled at the unwanted attention. "Why all the fuss," he protested under his breath. Good old Bill, true to his form, independent, stubborn, and not allowing anyone, even himself, to experience the fears simmering within. Vital signs, heart monitoring devices, and an intravenous drip with medications were already in place. Blood samples, more monitoring, a thousand questions, and more tests followed. If Bill seemed steady and calm before he arrived, his anxiety level increased as he was being treated in an emergency room that was unlike any building he had previously designed. To his surprise and delight, all the tests were negative, or so they seemed. Bill decided he should go home. "We want to keep you overnight for observation," the doctor instructed. This was not a part of Bill's agenda. Again, he felt out of control.

Put another way, Bill found it easier to leave than to admit there was the possibility of having a real problem with his heart. Something had to be let go, mainly his resistance to care, and therefore, the acceptance of his own vulnerability and his need for help. Going home to what was familiar seemed easier than to enter into the unknown journey of illness. The doctor looked Bill sternly in the eyes and said, "Yes, you can leave, but I cannot guarantee that you would be alive by the time you get out to your son's car in the parking lot." Needless to say, Bill did stay overnight and learned something about self-care. Something within Bill had to metaphorically die, so he could live. This was his rite of passage, which from a Campbellian point of view, becomes those trials and struggles that a hero faces "that demand a change in the patterns not only of the conscious but also of the unconscious life"[74] How important it is to learn and to be willing to let go. Follow up tests showed he needed open heart surgery to fix three heart blockages.

The Mortal God Asclepius

Asclepius, the Roman name for the Greek God of Medicine, Asklepios, is as mysterious as the art of medicine itself. Spanning more than 1,000 years of history, from primordial sagas and heroic tales to a deified mortal and god, the legend of Asclepius more than any other Greek or Roman god captures the imagination and needs of those who suffer and seek his help. There is a metamorphosis in the development of the myth of Asclepius. He emerged first in Thessaly, Kos, and Epidaurus where his Asklepios, or temples, were built and became known throughout Greece and later in Rome.

The Oracle of Apollo is at the heart of the healing rituals throughout ancient times. When someone was sick, they did not seek a human clinician alone, but a divine one since it was believed that illness was caused by the gods and therefore, it could only be cured by a god or other divine action. How often even today, when one is faced with a traumatic event, one questions "Is God punishing me?" Healing becomes a divine and sacred action, and when it is vested with such dignity, caregiving has the inexhaustible advantage that it can be vested with a healing power. This insight is critical in understanding the archetypal energies of the Wounded Healer, critical in that the wound itself is vested with its own healing power, suggests C.J. Groesbeck.[75]

Asclepius is singled out as one of the Greek gods who experiences death. His fame, like no other god, remained alive until the 3rd century of the Common Era, when other deities faded and were lost. His symbols of a snake and staff continue to be the emblem of modern medicine and healing. Asclepius is divinized as a mortal-god and even later, during the first centuries of Christianity, was seen as a prototype of Jesus Christ. Parallels to Asclepius and Christ began to emerge early. Both were born of divine fathers and human mothers. Each was raised by foster fathers, Chiron and Joseph. Each suffered and died and descended into Hades. Each rose and ascended to the heavens. The serpent, a symbol of transformation, becomes a symbol for each.

While there were these similarities, there is one remarkable difference between the portrayal in art of Asclepius and Christ. While Asclepius, whose curing mission resembled that of Christ, it is important to note that there are no pictures of Asclepius shown in the act of healing. Christ, on the other hand, is shown actually working the miraculous cures he was said to perform. He is shown touching those he is curing, the leper, the paralytic, and the blind. The miracles of Asclepius were recorded in stone, while those of Christ were shown in tender detail in incessant replication on tombs, reliefs, tableware, clothing and in the Christian Scriptures.[76]

Ancient physicians like Asclepius were considered to participate in divine acts of healing. Kerényi suggests that it is the physician's awareness of the divinity and sacredness of his healing art "which transplants wisdom into medicine and medicine into wisdom. And the physician who is a lover of wisdom is the equal to a god"[77] Again we have humankind's attempt to understand the sacred or transcendent aspect of the one who cares, of the one who is the caregiver. Said differently, the energy of our call as caregivers empowers us in developing the skills of our profession. Gods do appear in our acts of hospitality. We do entertain them. We do experience the sacredness of our work, even if only dimly.

Christ: The New Divine Physician

With the rise of Christianity, Christ becomes the new divine physician, the Wounded Healer who takes upon himself the woundedness of humankind. He becomes the Suffering Servant of Yahweh as prefigured by Isaiah 53:5. He is lifted up for all to see (John 3:14) and becomes metaphorically like Asclepius, the divine serpent, a worm and no man, whose image becomes a sign of hope to those who enter into the underworld of darkness, woundedness, illness, and sin. Henri Nouwen describes how the mythology of the Wounded Healer is present in Hassidic stories and in the Christian symbolism of the Crucifixion, and how the extraordinary healing presence and power of healers was attributed to weakness or woundedness within them.[78]

An Image of Disfigurement

The wounded figure of Christ became more than an image to Katherine, who was rushed to the hospital with internal bleeding. She was visiting some friends when she collapsed. At the hospital an ovarian tumor was discovered and immediately she was sent to surgery. During her recuperation, I came to visit to see how she was coping. She talked about the shock of the surgery, the fact that she had a hysterectomy and how she struggled with her own image of being a woman. She felt not only a physical disfigurement, but also an emotional and spiritual one. I listened as Katherine continued: "I know in time, I will heal and understand more fully the mystery of wholeness. At this time, however, I find myself grieving and knowing something that was a part of me is no longer there. I woke up crying during the night and in the empty space I experienced, my eyes caught a glimpse of a crucifix hanging on the wall. A calming voice came over me as words not my own, and yet, so very much my own, echoed through my lips: 'You understand. You understand what and how I am feeling.' Reflecting on the disfigurement that Christ experienced caught me by surprise. I simply do not know what I would have done if I didn't see that crucifix hanging on the wall."

Katherine identified with a disfigured Christ, a God who suffers. She was able to identify her own suffering with that of another whose mutilated body hung before her. Naked, abandoned, lost in the agony of suffering and feeling no longer totally human, she felt abandoned and at times, forsaken. Paraphrasing the words of Psalm 22, Kathy felt less than a woman, maybe like one of the lowliest of creatures, like a worm and no longer human. The psalmist uses the image of a worm to describe this disfigurement. "O my God, I cry by day, but you do not answer; and by night but find no rest. But I am a worm and hardly human, scorned by others and despised by the people (Ps. 22:3, 7).

From the Depths

The worm is a metaphor for one whose body is mangled and disfigured and no longer considered human. Woundedness brings destruction to both body and Soul. Woundedness also gives insight into healing and transformation. A worm crawls in the underworld of the earth bringing destruction in the consumption of waste materials. At the same time, it brings new life with the aeration and fertilization of the soil. This chthonic creature becomes another symbol for the primordial serpent that crawls on the earth and in Hindu mythology is close to its heartbeat. Like the serpent hanging from the staff of Moses in the Hebrew Scriptures, bringing healing to those who look upon it, this Christ-serpent hangs on the wood of the Cross in a way similar to the ancient Asklepian symbol of healing and transformation.

This icon captures not only the image of the suffering of Christ, but attributes to him the title of the servant of Yahweh. This image and title summarize those ancient images that were prefigured in older spiritual traditions. Important aspects of this icon are the association of the staff or rod and the serpent. The staff symbolizes authority and the tree of life, while the serpent is associated with healing and transformation and with Christ hanging on the wood of the Cross. The ancient divine archetype of healing becomes amplified again in the person of Jesus who becomes the worm and no man. Healing is accomplished by both gazing upon, as well as the recognition of one's woundedness.

This is both the paradox and the mystery that is hidden within this ancient symbol of healing. The symbol becomes the icon of Soul-making, that creative place where beauty is active and reflected. So universal is this symbol that it has become the modern symbol of medicine, the caduceus. The power of the wound draws out the healer function that is dormant in the one who is suffering, as well as it activates and supports the caregiver.

Parzival's Quest as a Wounded Healer

"What's in a name?" Juliet asks Romeo in William Shakespeare's Romeo and Juliet (II, ii). A name identifies and is linked to cultural and mythological stories that often reveal a hidden meaning or a special identity. The name Isabel, for example, means one who is pledged to God, while Edward connotes a guardian or protector of riches. Interesting then, is the 12th century German story of Parzival, whose name means piercedthrough-the-heart."[79] Piercing implies a woundedness that may be emotional, psychological, spiritual, and physical. Piercing involves suffering while learning what the call to adventure entails.

Parzival is given a clue about his heroic journey, one in which his suffering will assist him in overcoming his arrogance and pride while moving toward an interior attitude of humility and compassion. Only then will Parzival be able to understand the Grail question and become the Grail King. Being pierced through the heart is another image for being a wounded healer, as Parzival reflects on the incurable wound of the Grail King Anfortas and on his own.

Heart Intelligence

As discussed earlier, prior to the late 17th century, the human heart was considered the center of a person and the core of imagination. As the symbolic unity of intellect, feelings, and intuition, the heart was the agent of circulation in Ancient Greece, the Hindu seat of Brahma, the Islamic throne of God, and the Christian kingdom of God where the pilgrim travels in the primordial state where God dwells.[80] Parzival represents a different image, a heart that suffers, one that is linked to the earthly endeavors of life. With the discovery of autopsies by Harvey, the heart was understood from a technological perspective as a pump, a change that moved it from mythos to logos. The heart becomes mechanical and the idea of the sacred mystery is lost. "How can all that the heart symbolizes such as the courage to live, the center of one's strength and passion, love, feelings, the locus of one's Soul, and identity, how can all this be held in the hands of the physician or the coroner?" argues James Hillman.[81]

There are physicality and embodiment in the beat of the heart and a sense of being grounded. Listen to the tapping of orchestrated fingers against stretched animal skins synchronizing with the heartbeat of the earth. Ancient music comes alive stirring the depths of one's Soul. The beat of the heart reminds us how the heart circulates the integrated life of nature, humankind, and the cosmos. This "heart intelligence" comes alive when there is a simultaneous knowing and loving by means of imagining.[82] The pilgrimage of Dante guided by Virgil and motivated by the love of Beatrice in *The Divine Comedy* is such an example of a simultaneous knowing and loving. Knowing and loving, logos and mythos, create images that give life and inspire. At this juncture of reflection, one experiences enchantment. Campbell calls this process *aesthetic arrest* which is "that enchantment of the heart by which the mind is arrested and raised above desire and loathing in the luminous stasis of aesthetic pleasure"[83] Part of the power of symbols and myths is that they "enchant" those who are willing to engage them.

Let's focus again on the original call of the caregiver whose response to the one in need demands a focus and skill to be immersed in the situation at hand. This focus is grounded in compassion, the ground of true morality, as we participate first in responding to the pain of the other, and then in the alleviation of that pain.[84]

This was the case when I responded to an urgent page. Louisa, the daughter whose mother was dying, called for the chaplain. Overwhelmed by conflicting feelings as she held vigil with her mother, she asked for support and guidance. I knew that a compassionate presence was important. However, the loss and grief Louisa felt over her mother dying brought to light a deeper loss she had experienced as a child. "I am so angry at my mother I want to kill her," she sobbed. Talk about the need for direct questions and more active listening! Louisa then told the story of her mother's brother molesting her when she was 10 years old. More compassion, and more listening. "She's dying now. Little good that would do!" Louisa moaned. "Why didn't she believe me? Why didn't she protect me?"

Feelings of rage, sadness, and guilt brought her to the stark realization of the depth of the loss she was now experiencing. She had lost her mother's protection many years ago, and her mother's impending death ignited a long-smothering flame. In these moments of listening, I knew that the process of recovery would be longer than the time I had with Louisa. The beginning of the end began that evening in the compassion I felt and realizing that although the unraveling of her complex grieving would take longer, what was important was the presence I could offer Louisa. Her uncle had died, she was already seeing a counselor. What she needed now was a validation that her feelings were appropriate.

The journey to healing was indeed complex as daughter and mother now faced each other with only moments remaining to possibly begin a process of forgiveness. Despite her conflicting emotions and feelings towards her mother, Louisa was able to show her love, holding her hand until she died. Holding these conflicting emotions of Louisa, as well as creating the space for her to discover and respond to the different levels of grief she was experiencing, was both a challenge and seasoned skill for me.

St. John of God: Wounded for Others

Being wounded, metaphorically and realistically, is a part of being human. What draws me to the life of John of God is his ability to be comfortable with his own vulnerability, limitations, and woundedness. While the word archetype would have been foreign to John, nonetheless, he had an uncanny way in how he reached out to those who were sick and abandoned on the streets of sixteenth-century Granada, Spain. Metaphorically, I believe he intuitively understood the universal energies of a wounded healer in how he was drawn to alleviate the pain of those he served. Realistically, John, in the here and now, had the ability to understand his own struggles and sufferings, and therefore have compassion for those in need.

The turning point in his life came one night as he attended a service at the local church. A sermon by the renowned Spanish preacher John of Avila sent John into the streets crying for mercy and forgiveness, overwhelmed by the experience of God's love. Spit upon, bullied, and roughly handled, he was considered to be mad as he tore at his clothes and rolled on the ground. Friends took him to the Royal Hospital where he was shackled and placed in the psychiatric ward. As he regained his strength and insight, he was allowed to help others at the hospital. As mercy was shown him, he began to reach out to other inmates.

Once released from the hospital, John started a hospice to take in the poor, abandoned, and the less-desirable of the city. He went around the city begging for alms to support his work saying, "Do good to yourselves by doing good to others." As his charitable works grew, so did his reputation. He was thought to be either of God or mad.[85] The ancient, universal, and archetypal energies of the wounded healer, of angels and gods appearing when offered hospitality, came alive for John with those who suffered. As the wounded Christ became a model of compassion to John, he strove to become a model to those who suffered and were ill.

Two different events reveal how John's practice of hospitality entertained gods and angels. One evening he came across a wounded beggar lying in the streets. He attempted to pick him up and carry him to his hospice. Yet he couldn't. Finally, he tried again and found that he was able. He looked and realized he was being assisted by the Archangel Raphael, whose name means "God heals." This scene was captured in paint by the 16th-century painter Bartolome Murillo who attempted to portray how divine energies and strengths assist one. In a moment of weakness, John found the interior archetypal strength and grace to care.

On another occasion, John was washing the feet of one of the residents in the hospice. As he continued to wash, John noticed wounds on the resident's feet and looking up, realized he was washing the feet of Christ. The one who was wounded became a healer to the one washing his feet. Whether Christ actually appeared or not, the insight John experienced was a reminder of the sacredness of his work. Angels and gods did appear. What is inspiring to me as a caregiver, and former member of the Hospitaller Brothers of St. John of God, and what I find to be universal in most caregivers, is that John, while being locked up and shackled in a mental institution, in one of his darkest moments, discovered his call to service. Why do we fear to be vulnerable, when in reality, in the midst of our vulnerability, we may discover our strengths? The following story captures the experience of James who, in discovering the ramifications of a diagnosis of myeloma, was thrust into a strange and unfamiliar world. At the core of his being, he struggled with the tension of experiencing his need for help while remaining in charge as best he could.

Drifting Out to Sea, Yet Moored by Family

The complexity of both the medical center and his diagnosis led James into a dark place of uncertainty. Unanswered questions moved him beyond impatience to a mild state of fear and anxiety as he lay in his hospital bed. The currents of the day, such as his tests being postponed, the doctors not showing up, the idleness of what appeared to waste time and not getting things done efficiently, sent James drifting off into an unknown sea. Dealing with a new diagnosis of cancer was difficult enough but waiting to learn to its extent and possible treatments seemed more unnerving than the actual diagnosis. "Mark," James remarked to his nurse, "I feel like I have drifted out to sea, without a compass, without knowing which direction to go." James found an image to convey what he found difficult to express, his own lack of control, ambiguity, and vulnerability.

The tidal wave of uncertainty that surrounded him sent him to a place that was unfamiliar, a place where he experienced doubt and uncertainty. Within this liminal space of "betwixt and between," James waited, drifting, and numb to the possibility of finding a compass hidden within him. Insight gradually came as he became conscious of his wife Amy sitting beside him holding his hand. His daughter, Carol, a research analyst for a drug company doing trials for cancer patients, already had arranged a consultation with the leading cancer expert on myeloma in the state. His son, Scott, who worked out of state, was arriving the next weekend to assist with chores around the house. Simultaneously, James found himself drifting and yet being moored by the life-line his wife, son and daughter were providing. This new world of liminality was messy, uncertain, and unnerving. A threshold of affliction had been crossed. A threshold that we, as caregivers often face when we find ourselves drifting into uncharted situations. Along with the professional caregivers providing care for James, Amy, Carol, and Scott, also joined the team of caregivers.

Swept Across the Threshold

Illness is a threshold that one crosses involuntarily as one often feels caught in a receding tide. James's experience of drifting out to sea is such an example. The threshold that he crossed separated him from the world he knew as he entered the hospital. The doors of the medical center might be likened to the jaws of a whale that seemed to swallow him into the darkness of both his inner world and that of the medical establishment, quite similar to Jonah descending into the underworld in finding himself in the belly of a whale (Jonah 1:17). Without understanding the implications of this passage, James passed through the liminal jaws, the permeable wall and the artificial barrier we impose between myth and reality.[86] Questions such as what is real or imagined arise. Similar to the curtain separating one hospital bed from another, this questioning restrains yet captures the realities on both sides of the curtain. The permeable partition that the curtain signifies holds the tension of opposites between what is a myth and what is reality.

In the midst of the angst James felt, he found an image to express an experience that was unknown to him, the image of drifting out to sea. While in itself it expresses movement, drifting also became an image that grounded James in the reality of his experience as a person with cancer. Some things were beginning to change. James was totally unaware that he too would be changing in this process. The James that he knew was beginning to experience a metamorphosis: self and ego were in the process of dying and being renewed.

Relevance for Today

In 1951, Jung first used the term "Wounded Healer." Reflecting on his life's experience, he came to believe that in any ongoing relationship a doctor has with his client that the whole personality of both client and doctor is called into play. While he specifically speaks of the time-honored doctor-patient relationship, we, as caregivers, can apply the same understanding to ourselves. He writes that "the doctor is effective only when he himself is affected [...] only the wounded physician heals. But when the doctor wears his personality like a coat of armor, he has no effect."[87] Reflect again for a moment the difference between just doing your job versus the call you experience that motivates you as a caregiver.

Common Usage

Recently the term "wounded healer" has been used synonymously with burnout or impairment of caregivers in the healing professions, comments Len Sperry.[88] He recognizes that the term is not new and has been associated with a sacred tradition across several cultures throughout the ages. The relationship between woundedness and healing is a truth recognized in myths and rituals of traditional cultures throughout the world. Serge Daneault asks the question whether this archetype can assist physicians. He recognizes the Wounded Healer as one who has gone through suffering and as a result of that experience becomes a source of great wisdom, healing, and inspiration for others.[89]

The physician becomes a healer as his technical skills are guided by his experiences and self-reflection. Dr. Martin Lipp adds: "My wounds become my spectacles, helping me to see what I encounter with empathy and a grateful sense of privilege"[90] The patient facilitates the doctor's own healing through both of these discovering those interior resources that allow healing and transformation to occur. Each is involved in a process that activates a healer function from within. Finding Soul invites the wound to speak, holding and listening tenderly and compassionately to the promptings from within.

Conclusion

The psychic energies of the Wounded Healer contain the ability for both the caregiver and for the one being served to hold what seems impossible to be held. The healer, on the one hand, must first recognize his or her own wounds so as to make space and understand the woundedness of the other. So necessary is this inner work of the caregiver that without it, there is a danger that healing may not occur, not only for the one in need but also for the caregiver. An understanding of one's personal woundedness, suffering, and illness appears to be a prerequisite for the caregiver and for the one in need.

Empathy and compassion are drawn from these experiences because an awareness of woundedness "is a prerequisite for taking on the role of healer" suggests Christine Downing.[91] The miracle of participating in the archetypal energies of the Wounded Healer is that the one who suffers discovers the capacity for and the possibility of healing and of one's human dignity being restored through the encounter with the caregiver. Concurrently, in facilitating this process, the caregiver rediscovers his or her dignity being restored and renewed. Face to face with life, the caregiver is challenged to find meaning in the mystery of caregiving. There is an interchange between the caregiver as host and the client as a stranger in need. Creating that interior space to receive the stranger, is an interior act of the Soul. So too is creating the time, energy, and space for the caregiver to understand his or her experiences.

My intention throughout this work, but especially in this chapter, is to invite you to explore the variety of emotions, reflections, and reactions you may experience as a caregiver. In Chapter Seven: Cultivating the Soul's Garden, we will explore what most of us fear and avoid, listening to the stirrings of our Soul.

Timeout: A Moment of Reprieve

1. Was there a particular insight or question that emerged during your reading of this chapter?

2. Do you relate to being a wounded healer?

3. What, in your service to others, excites you and gives you joy?

4. What animates and sustains you in your profession?

5. Are you conscious of your strengths that support and nourish you?

Chapter 7 - Tending the Soul's Garden: Reclaiming the Art of Reflection

Introduction

This chapter addresses a skill we all have as caregivers - our ability to reflect. We do it all the time in our professional and personal lives. We plan, explore options, and execute them. All are opportunities for reflection. Each project, each experience, each job well done can lead one to pause and ponder. These reflections may lead one to change a procedure, or a policy, or to make future decisions. Change is what occurs outside one's self. Tending to the Soul's garden implies an interior change or even a transformation. William Bridges argues that we culturally often confuse the two. Change is situational, like deciding to develop a new skill, to move the furniture around, to paint your office a different color, or to accept a promotion.

Transformation, on the other hand, is about interior changes, about listening to one's Soul, about learning from one's experiences, commonly called a change of heart. It is not a static event but one that is dynamic and implies movement. Transformation is being on a hero's journey where one gains insight and a psychological awareness about one's inner reorientation and self-redefinition that needs to occur for the change to work.[92] Noteworthy is that Bridges' understanding of the process of transformation is similar to the hero's journey as outlined by Joseph Campbell and discussed earlier in Chapter Three. The hero's journey consists of a call, a leave-taking where one descends into the netherworld where the hero faces trials, uncertainties, monsters, and chaos. The journey challenges the hero or heroine to win the boon, the prize to achieve a new status and to make a return victoriously.

I like how Bridges realizes that the process of transformation is dynamic. The first phase is an ending to something or life event that can be considered a positive or negative experience. Take for example a promotion, or an inheritance, the birth of a child, going away to college. Other's may include the death of a family member, the ending of a marriage, being laid off from work or suffering a traumatic event such as a flood, hurricane, or wildfire. Each of these events leads the participant into phase two, a period of uncertainties, distress, and chaos. The death of a family member leads one to a new worldview without them. The ending of a marriage leaves one with the uncertainty of the future, as does being made redundant at work. Traumatic events challenge one's interior belief systems as something has radically changed such as one's safety. Finally, the journey may lead one to the third phase of transformation which is a new beginning such as a new job, a new experience, a new freedom, and awareness of one's interior strengths. In summary, there is an ending, a wondering, concluding with a new beginning.[93]

An Innate Skill

Caregivers face this day in and day out as life teaches them the pains and joys of being human. One cannot remain neutral, as caregiving has its way of transforming the caregiver. Each event, each act of service, each encounter with the one being served has an impact on the caregiver. Most of the times, the experience leads the caregiver to a greater appreciation of who they are as caregivers. Sometimes, the caregiver partakes in traumatic events that may take more time to debrief and more time with self-care. Sometimes, the experience of these traumatic events leads to the caregiver experiencing different symptoms of PTSD.

Who doesn't appreciate a job well done in knowing that you give yourself so selflessly in the work you do. How about your experience of savoring or lingering over a glass of red wine after a homemade pasta dish? These are moments that are borne out of our experiences, the wonderful events in our lives. Yet each of these experiences may also be transformative, the acceptance of appreciation may lead one to a greater work ethic and lingering over a glass of wine may lead one to greater insight and the experience of gratitude. The skills we have learned as caregivers were not taught in a vacuum but developed and improved by reflecting on our experiences. It is how we learn. It is also how our lives can be transformed.

In your career can you remember how you first felt as a student nurse or teacher, a new member of the emergency medical team (EMT), your experience as a first responder, or a physician intern still wet behind the ears, compared to how you feel now? There was a call to service, a new beginning, and then delving into the work, a wondering, an exploration, challenges, growth, mistakes, and trials. Then there was the experience of achievement, a new beginning, an arrival at the accomplishment, of certitude, and learned wisdom. Insights gleaned from your experiences have made you a better caregiver. This is the miracle of caregiving. We, who seek to heal, the wounded healers that we are, are transformed in the act of healing. Without any promptings or manuals, we were taught the process of reflection. Reflection is the tool that cultivates the garden of our Soul by tending to those memories and images that reveal a history of who we are. I remember one of my first experiences as a graduate nurse. Maestro! A little music, it's time for a moment of reverie.

A Lighthearted Lesson

One of my most light-hearted experiences as a graduate nurse was when I was assisting a physician intern at the bedside. The patient's gastric feeding tube needed to be replaced. Simple. We discussed the procedure with David, the patient as we were also preparing the treatment table. The doctor then cut the stitch holding the tube in place and the tube was easily removed. As we were getting ready to insert a new one, turning towards the treatment table, David decided to let us know he was still in charge despite his recent suffering a stroke that affected his gag reflex. He decided to cover the stoma or opening, with his arm. When we turned ready to insert the tube, the patient expanded his belly so the indentation of his belly button appeared to be the stoma. In a flash, we knew this was not the intended opening. Almost instantly the patient began to laugh and picked up his arm. I think I chuckled more than the intern as we realized there was a vast difference between a surgical stoma and the depression of his belly button. We both learned not to take things too seriously, as the David provided a bit of comic relief for each of us. In your repertoire of experiences, can you bring forth out of the storeroom of your life, experiences that bring a smile to your face?

The Caregiver as Active Participant

Consider for a moment the different insights you experienced in reading the preceding chapters. Do you remember our discussion in Chapter One about reflection being a process of stepping back and reviewing one's experience and memories of an event? Sometimes stepping back brings to mind pleasant, even joyful experiences. Other times, we may be confronted with experiences both professionally and personally that are sad, even painful. Our Soul has a way of bringing up issues and memories that need healing, such as the Dance of Caregiving that we explored in Chapter One.

As such, sometimes the caregiver is engaged on many different levels, one the skilled tactician, another actively involved with the client, and finally, one engaged in the exploration of one's experience of the event. Let me give you an example of such an experience when I was the participant, almost like in a Greek Tragedy, actively listening to the one affected, and then realizing, I needed time to explore what was happening within me because of this experience. The call to visit a patient, the descent, into the experience of the patient's mother, and the outcome, a new understanding about self-care.

Personal Suffering Masks as Anger

When I knocked on the door, I thought this would be a routine visit welcoming a new patient to the rehabilitation unit. I was greeted by the mother of the patient, Mrs. Morales, who immediately recognized me from our encounter three weeks ago when her daughter, Angela was admitted to the intensive care unit. She commented even before I could introduce myself, "Do you remember me?" Immediately, I recalled the patient care conference the neurosurgeon called to discuss treatment options regarding Angela who was suffering from a cerebral hemorrhage. As we discussed the meeting and the outcome of the conference, something triggered Mrs. Morales to engage in an outburst of anger over the neurosurgeon. She was furious, even vitriolic. I just listened, realizing it was not about me, a trap many caregivers find themselves in when confronted with anger. Mrs. Morales' anger and frustration were a cover, I surmised, most likely for the deep pain she was feeling over her daughter's diagnosis: paralyzed at the age of thirty-four. As a pastoral counsellor, I guess she trusted me enough to vent her frustration, giving her permission to cry out, even to God.

My intuition was to simply listen, knowing that her anger was authentic and needed a voice. Not many of us, growing up or later in a workplace situation, were rewarded for expressing anger. Granted there are appropriate ways to express our anger, but damn it, the first step is to admit we are angry, and secondly, to be able to express it. No one I know likes to be the scapegoat for another's anger. Likewise, there is a responsibility by the one expressing the anger to be able to understand the root causes of it and find an adequate way to express it. I knew, given the allotted time, the best I could do was to listen. Not everything would be taken care of in one pastoral visit. Nor did it have to be. It was enough that she could voice her real feelings that most likely had been brewing ever since her daughter's accident. I just happened to be the person at the right time for the eruption to occur. Lucky me, I thought. Yet how often we, as caregivers, might blame ourselves for such an outburst when indeed it has nothing to do with us. I don't know what I said, or how I left the room. I just remember walking down the hall which seemed longer than usual, leaving the rehabilitation unit and entering the hospital. Something in me urged me to speak with one of my colleagues on the fifth floor.

Before I could even say anything, Susanne smiled as I was coming out of the elevator. When I came more into view her smile turned to concern and even alarm. "Ed," Susanne remarked, "you look terrible. What happened?" I remember distinctly putting my hands together over my head and like holding a trowel, I began making scraping hand movements telling Susanne that I must scrape all the anger off of me. Actually, I said, "Susanne, give me a moment to scrap all this shit off of me, it is not about me." I learned that day, that caregivers often become the target or scapegoat for clients or their family members to vent. There were many lessons I learned as a caregiver that afternoon, such as active listening, presence, and the realization that I did not have to fix anything. The question was whether I was willing to do the interior work to further explore the lessons. It was a clear choice, was I hospitable enough to welcome one who masquerades her Soul pain with anger. I knew that I had to welcome the client where she was, even if I have to navigate through the sludge of angry feelings.

Trusting Your Insights

While I was an active participant in the example above, my role was to welcome the new patient to the hospital and do a spiritual care assessment. Unable to speak, I still remember the perplexed expression on Angela's face during the exchange. I also became involved with and experienced the trauma of the patient's mother. I knew intuitively her anger was not about me. That insight about not blaming myself developed over a period of some time. However, reflecting on my experience, even now leads me to more insight and discovery. For example, why did she feel safe to vent her frustrations with me? Was she crying out to God, who I, as a pastoral counsellor informally represented? Our experiences lead us to gather our thoughts, to become aware, if not interiorly silent, as insights are borne that teach us wisdom.

There is a scene in the movie "Children of a Lesser God" that reveals this societal tension of expressing anger. Sarah Norman struggles to express her anger, anger she has stuffed over the years over being deaf and the rejection she experienced by her father. She reaches the boiling point when she is encouraged to move out of her comfort zone by James a professor at the school. Desperate for not knowing how to sort out her anger, and at the same time falling in love with James, Sarah runs away to her estranged mother, only to be followed by James. When he asks why she left him, Sarah says in so many words,

"I thought that if I faced the anger raging within me, it would kill me. Instead, I learned I am more than my anger and I can face it."[94]

Reflection is at the Heart of Being Human

Did you find yourself daydreaming and gaining insight as you listened to the frustrations and anger of a devoted mother in the preceding story? Were there stories in the earlier chapters which mirrored something about yourself? Did you discover an event that radically had an effect on you and might have been transformative? There may have been something in your life that ended, something that led you to explore a new beginning. Did the questions at the end of each chapter help you in exploring insights that may have been hidden? My point is this: reflection is at the heart of being human. We do it all the time. It is not a skill reserved for monks, nuns, or mystics in monasteries alone, but an interior process that we as humankind possess and like everything else we do, we need to practice. "It is the spark within us," suggests Thomas Merton, "that ignites our intuition and flourishes most purely right in the middle of the ordinary."[95]

Images then Words

During one of my pastoral counseling classes the instructor asked the class to choose an image that represented an area of personal growth. Why an image, I wondered? I began to question the question. Images that appear in our consciousness similar to the joy of a two-year-old recognizing the difference between a teddy bear and rabbit or an experience of gratitude remembering when you met your partner or spouse, or a moment of reverence, maybe with hands clasped, or prostrate before what seems like the Holy of Holies. Images of trauma, fear, or traumatic events may also come to mind that like the tip of an iceberg, reveal hidden and painful emotions. Reflection allows images to emerge. Action, camera, and roll as representations or pictures emerge in our consciousness. These images are not those we see externally as seeing a picture in a magazine. These are interior images that emerge from memories and experiences.

I remember when I started a diet a few years ago. Even before I started, an image of skinny me appeared. I loved skinny me. I was filled with joy and remembered when I could turn sideways, and you couldn't see me. Tall and thin I was until I started to grow east and west instead of north and south. That was before my metabolism changed. I envisioned going on a spending spree since I was already down a few sizes. The images had their own stories even before I could express them in words or develop a plan of action. This is how imagination manifests itself in a variety of ways, as a diet elicited the image of skinny me and how much I yearned to be skinny me again.

The image appeared first and then the words. Earlier we discussed how the Ulanovs' maintain how imagination comes into play in our daily lives and how it expresses psychic life "which speaks first in images before it speaks in words."[96] How often do we get tongue-tied trying to articulate an experience that is symbolized through an image, struggling to find the words to express what we are experiencing? Somehow, we have to listen to what the image wants to say to us which means we must also create an attitude of listening. Not that this is foreign to us, but like a muscle, we need to exercise it. This was the task at hand presented by the professor. Find an image and allow it to speak as it had a language of its own which leads one to meditation and reflection.

The second part of the exercise was to ask the class if they would support me with the goals I set up. Like most caregivers, I was often too busy to stop and reflect on an area of growth or improvement, let alone openly discuss it with my peers. Sound familiar? There was some comfort, however, in knowing that each member of the class was also charged with the same task. We were given about ten minutes, which at first seemed like an hour, to be silent and be attentive to what images came to mind. Oh my God, I can already hear the moans and groans of each member in the room. Silence was not a practice that most of us were familiar with. I was also in a transitional period and had been sorting out a few career choices. Some things needed to be changed while other new beginnings, though exciting, also presented a challenge. Again, the call, the journey, and then a new beginning. However, remaining in the status quo, was no longer an option.

Sprinkle Fertilizer Around Its Roots

Somehow, the ground had been prepared as the image of a peach tree came to light. I remember it was cut back a bit, yet there were new shoots developing around the base of the tree, promises of more fruit. Dreams of eating those ripened peaches that combined a taste of sweetness interlaced with a certain tartness, again an image, seemed to slip into the numinous realm of my consciousness. Simultaneously, a voice within seemed to say, "Not to worry, just dig around its roots, and add a little fertilizer and all will be well." The image of the fruit tree led to other images of new shoots and ripened peaches, of the tilled ground, and lastly the star of the kaleidoscope, fertilizer.

Imagine, Fertilizer! Fertilizer to be spread around my roots and how did this correlate with personal growth? First things first, I mused, let's explore what fertilizer actually does? Fertilizer, as you know, has a challenging aroma, yet it simply provides nutrients for plants and trees, and crops to grow. So, I needed, metaphorically, some fertilizer. But then what? Not that I had visions of entertaining the possibility of rolling around on a dung heap. There is no time to take a deep breath, as the farmer within instinctively knows what not to do. I have clear recollections of using it in my garden as well as almost gasping for air as I drove past the meandering fields along the central California coast preparing for the planting of lettuce, broccoli, spinach, cauliflower, tomatoes and cabbage to name a few.

My mind raced as I knew the next step was to share this image with the thirty members of my class. Was this the only meaning of fertilizer? How could I translate this in a practical way? Was the fertilizer I needed something like developing new goals, spending more time in self-care, understanding my own interior values and processes or listening more attentively to the inner promptings of my Soul? Somehow, I needed more time as the restlessness within me vanished. I was on to something, wanting to go deeper. These musings within me, however, were silenced by hearing my name called. It was now my turn to share the fruits of my musings with my classmates.

There is an irony about my words, sharing the fruits of my reflections as I told the story of a fruitless tree and how it reminded me of a passage in the Christian Scriptures.[97] Then there was silence, a pregnant pause, as I remember. I looked around the room stumbling to get the words out after the story I just related, and then I said: "Each of you, my classmates, are the fertilizer I need to spread around my roots. Now don't take this literally, that is about fertilizer, just a metaphor that I need nutrients from a variety of resources including you to support, challenge, and cajole me during this coming year." I began to smile as others did too. This was about tending the garden of my Soul.

There weren't the gasps that I expected, but a sincere understanding, even a few laughs. Any type of personal growth involves two factors, one personal and one collectively. While there is an individual aspect to growth, something that one holds very close to one's self, any reflective process is enhanced by the support of another, be they a spouse, friend, pastor or counselor. While caregivers may experience the invitation to reflect more on a particular event, it is often difficult to ask for help or seek the support of their colleagues. Remember Allison's comment earlier that many first responders refer to critical access debriefing as "the crybabies club". Where did we learn that we have to "tough it" by ourselves? Tending to my Soul's garden is an ongoing task, one of attentiveness, one of careful listening, one of reaching out and one of patient watchfulness.

The Reflection Urge

It is, in the midst of what we do, within the ordinary happenstance of our lived experiences, insights emerge that lead us to moments of reverie and reflection. Reflecting is a spontaneous experience, as if we're caught up and lost in the moment, a sort of time out which takes us to different places of wonder and excitement, or to places of fear and painful memories. Sometimes one's insight needs time to germinate. That requires a patient suffering for fulfillment, somewhat like a gardener planting a late spring crop. Often surprised by new insights, one's Soul is active in creating new roots and foliage as the seed dies to give new life.

Gardening and tending to the cultivation of crops is an example of the ordinary. The image of the fruit tree I discussed earlier and digging around its roots only makes sense because of my questioning the image in the silence of my heart. Images have a voice of their own and need a hearing. Something difficult for modern humankind to understand is the art of listening and reflecting on what the image needs to say. So central is the reflection urge within us that Jung maintains it is one of the three psychic energies of the Soul.[98] Interesting, is how these energies pull us beyond their presence, so we can participate more in them. The image of a stump with new shoots, surrounded by some healthy fertilizer, became a portal leading me beyond the image to what the image wished to say. Simply, what did I need to do to focus on goals for self-care? What did surrounding my roots with fertilizer mean to me? Robert Bosnak says it best that the reflection urge moves us beyond the threshold that the image presents to a world of many possibilities.[99]

A Caregiver's Nightmare

Such was the experience of Daniel whose life came to a screeching halt when his phone rang one November morning. His partner had just left for a meeting five minutes before as Daniel was ready to jump into the shower. Something told him to look at his phone where there was a missed message from Robert. "Daniel, this is Robert, I'm so sorry, I just crashed the car. I am down the driveway next to the house on the side of the hill, and I called 911, I believe I'm ok." Imagine the different images that raced through Daniel's mind as he got dressed, called a friend, and raced to the site as quickly as he could.

The facts he knew were that Robert crashed the car down the hill and he was ok. It wasn't until he saw the car squeezed into a six-foot-wide space between a garage and a retaining wall that the image of the crash took on a deeper meaning. Paramedics were at the scene when Daniel arrived. His partner was already in an ambulance, after getting out of the car for fear it might explode. Water was leaking around the car because the car hit a water faucet on the side of the garage. Just the sight of the car, with a broken windshield, crushed fenders and damaged siding brought Daniel to tears.

The image, like the jaws of Jonah's whale, swallowed him into the darkness of its belly and evoked many possibilities. How did the car get there? What actually happened? How did Robert get out of the car?

Was he seriously hurt? Even more poignantly, how did he survive? Too many questions began cascading into immediate answers. Robert was safe and that's what mattered the most. There was just enough time for a quick hello as the ambulance took off to the hospital. The police and first responders tried to piece together what actually happened. Further answers would have to wait until Daniel met Robert in the emergency room.

Still in shock, after a myriad of tests, Robert tried to recount what had happened. When he backed up so he could make a left turn down their driveway, the accelerator stuck racing forward. If he went straight, he would go into a ravine, so he steered the car down the driveway. He tried the brakes, but they could not stop the car. At the end of the driveway, across the street was a storage shed and behind it a trailer. Not wanting to harm anyone, Robert steered the car to the right and began going down a steep roadway that led him out of the cul-de-sac. Again, he had no brakes and his speed kept increasing. He told me he was terrified hanging onto the steering wheel for dear life somewhat feeling like riding a bronco at a rodeo. Still trying to gain control, he slid through a wire fence into a field on the right side of the road. Before he knew it, the car hit a ditch on the descending hill and overturned two or three times, sliding into the space between the garage and a retaining wall. "I didn't black out and just held onto the steering wheel with my seat belt fashioned, terrified, but still in control." In a way he was still in control, Daniel commented, as Robert did steer the car to safety. In shock, he continued, "I knew I had to get out of the car as it was still running."

The impact of the accident echoed through each membrane and muscle of both Daniel and Robert. Using his caregiving instincts, Daniel realized it was time he reached out for help for himself and for Robert. Daniel needed to share with me, a close friend and also a coaching colleague what happened. As Daniel shared the story, I knew I needed to come over that evening. My role was simply to be present as best I could and listen.

Impact

Any traumatic shock to the nervous system is deeply felt within the person and is usually called muscle memory, as the impact is absorbed. Unlike the instinctual fight or flight response that releases adrenaline and biochemical reactions, when the body is overwhelmed or blocked by a traumatic experience, the body freezes trapping all the mobilized survival energy in the body suggests Diane Poole Heller.[100] So too, does the family and spouse experience the shock as if the impact was personally experienced. Daniel, shaking and in tears, kept repeating to me, "I just can't believe he is alive. I'm not ready to lose him." Each partner, as most caregivers do, experience traumatic events differently, yet what is common is the shared reality of feeling the impact of the trauma. So, let's break this down to better understand what the caregiver goes through after experiencing a traumatic event, or having the event retold to you, as happened in my case.

First of all, the facts of the event, in themselves, can speak volumes that seize one's imagination. Remember earlier the different images of the accident that raced through Daniel's imagination? Secondly, each image, like the slides of a PowerPoint, evoke different responses and feelings. They seem to have a life of their own. Some traumatic events may lead one to experience the symptoms of post-traumatic stress, where the chemical triggers of the brain, continue to present images as if the projector was stuck in the brain.

Pool Heller names different symptoms that can occur if the threat response, the impact of the accident, is not completed. These may include, anxiety such as restlessness and excessive energy, feeling disconnected, disorientation, fear of helplessness, hypervigilance, sexual apathy, exhaustion, physical pain, easily startled, triggered by similar events, and weight gain.[101]

Traumatic as the accident was, Daniel and Robert knew it was a time to do some debriefing. They asked me to become their life coach and with my help, they began to create their new normal, knowing intuitively what was before was shattered, and the foundation of their relationship, uncannily, had become stronger. Life had not ended, so they say, but it certainly changed for both Robert and Daniel. The accident had become a transformative event in their relationship, something that needed to be explored. Something ended that November morning on many levels and something new was beginning. It is in this liminal in-between space, between the ending and a new beginning where all the answers will be revealed.

Smacked Against a Telephone Pole

Listening to their story challenged me to reflect on my own experiences, an important exercise for each caregiver. As Robert and Daniel shared their story about their accident, as attentive as I was to their story, in the background of my consciousness was a faint voice seeking an audience about an auto accident I had three years ago. Both Daniel and Robert were pleased that I had a sense of understanding what they were feeling. When they asked me how I understood, I was able to share with them the impact I felt after hitting a telephone pole. I remember vividly how my car slid off an icy road to avoid hitting a deer. The impact was immediate as I slide into a telephone pole on the side of the curbless road. Smack! Then the shock of what just happened. How do you feel smack? A certain impact? A pushback from the pole, as it is certainly stronger than a sliding car. Even though only going about five miles an hour, the bumper and front right wheel were damaged.

My body still reverberates as I hear and still feel the crash, something that I continue to sort out. How do you feel hitting a wall? Sort of stupid, sort of surprised? Again smack, like hitting against a glass door of a department store. Yet, that is what I experienced similar to what Robert did. His car hit the side of a garage. That is what I felt as I listened to Daniel and Robert. The impact of hitting the telephone pole was buried deeply in the fibers of my body. Those feelings were hidden, yet now emerging, as I listened and became more empathetic to those feelings Robert must have had.

How often do we caregivers feel the traumatic events of another? How often may these remind us of our own traumatic experiences, and then what do we do? Sometimes we just stuff them, one after another, until one blindsides us because of an accumulation of the traumas and we experience the symptoms of compound PTSD. Both Daniel and

Robert set aside a block of time each day to explore together what had ended, what they were exploring, and what were the challenges for their new beginning. This led to listening more, of learning from each other, and able to take each day and be thankful. Addressing the experience together prevented some of the difficult symptoms that could lead to a diagnosis of PTSD as discussed earlier.

When You Speak of Soul, You Go Deeper

An understanding of Soul implies allowing the moment to take root and to reflect on how to nourish and sustain ourselves as caregivers. Why rush? Why the procrastination, I ask? Reflection is the work of the Soul that gathers and ponders those moments of reverie that connect inner and outer worlds. That is why I have chosen the pomegranate as a symbol of caregiving, as each caregiver allows the spark of insight to germinate. Just as the pomegranate reveals its secrets in due season, so too does the Soul refresh with insight and wisdom. Campbell calls this work, the work of reflection, the work of a mystic because one's Soul penetrates through the image and symbol. One gets lost where time and space seem to disappear. The caregiver enters into the land of many possibilities, to that place beyond its meaning, to silence, listening to that point of nothingness, where time and eternity meet."[102]

A Seasoned Mentor

Mentors are helpful in assisting younger caregivers learn the process of reflection. In a way, that is how they have become mentors. Mentors are those in one's profession who are experienced and trusted advisors. There is a generative aspect to a mentor, who because of their learned experience, wish to be guides for those earlier on their journeys. My experience in evaluating different mentorship programs has revealed that most stress the importance of a mentor to make a commitment to support the growth and development of an interested client and willingly share knowledge, skills, insights, experience and wisdom. Such is Dr. William Potter, a retired obstetrician, who became a mentor to thousands of medical students. He shared with me an experience he had early in his career to emphasize the importance of touch and its sacred ramifications in humanizing medical care. A routine medical examination became a linchpin to understanding his role in becoming sensitive and compassionate to the women he served.

Vulnerability and Ice

Both the chill in the room, and the impact of doing his first pelvic exam as a young medical student, had a lasting effect on later-to-be Dr. Potter forty years ago. Nothing was warm about the procedure with set protocols and the medical student entering the room with the patient already straddled in stirrups. The position itself seemed inhumane, exacerbating the uncomfortableness he felt. The intrusiveness of the exam had a lasting memory. No explanations to ease the apprehension of the patient. What this young student would remember was the apparent inhumanity, and the sterile cold instruments, and the cadre of instructors and other medical students in attendance. The image of this event as remembered by Potter had a life of its own balancing vulnerability and the science of medicine. The task, to learn to perform a pelvic examination, was so full of protocols that he often felt the patient got lost in the shuffle.

Even the most routine of such exams is something most women would rather not have. At the same time, I would argue that most men have no idea how such an exam borders on a razor-thin line of necessity versus violation, of an intrusive encounter experienced by the female patient during this procedure. Many things have changed over the years for this retired Maternal Health Practitioner, but the memory of this first encounter over forty years ago became the motivation to humanize the procedure in his practice. He made sure a nurse welcomed the patient, spent the time to go over the procedure, and prepare her for the examination.

Dr. Potter, would also welcome the patient, and explain each step as he did the examination. He emphasized to his medical students, interns and residents at the teaching hospital where he practiced, the importance of their sensitivity to and awareness of how the patient felt during this encounter. There was an intimacy involved that needed both a professional decorum and a caring awareness of the vulnerable nature of the patients. Dr. Potter was also eager to share how he failed to deal with the tension that arose in him during this early experience.

Self-care was not included in his medical training. He, along with many other physicians I interviewed, talked about the competition among physicians and about their fear of not knowing everything could lead to a perception that they were incompetent. This may also lead to an attitude of never giving up with patients who are dying, of trying everything possible, even if it causes harm to the patient. Physicians are trained in solving the "riddle" seeking a solution to the puzzle at all costs, even treating when futile.[103] Against this backdrop, it is even less commonplace to share one's vulnerability with a trusted friend or teammate.

It was difficult to admit his vulnerability regarding a particular case or the feelings that arose because of it. Stuffing his feelings led to broken relationships and turning to alcohol. Being involved in Alcoholic Anonymous not only saved his life but his career. He is kinder now, not only to his patients but also to himself. He came to realize that the ice that needed to be melted was within himself. Insight was learned from personal reflection on the importance of self-care. The experience was more than an event etched in his memory. The experience transformed him to be the doctor he is today. Reflection on his first experience as a medical student over forty years ago and other experiences since have made Dr. Potter the mentor that he has become.

Conclusion

In this chapter, Cultivating the Soul's Garden, I have stressed the importance that we, as caregivers, like the air that we breathe automatically, have the innate skill to reflect on our experiences. We are trained to do it professionally, but more often than not, we, as caregivers, spend little time on how our professional work affects us, and less time on cultivating our Soul's garden. The vignettes in this chapter were examples of the caregiver's experience of reflection. What is the glue, the motivation, the interior strengths that sustains caregivers? Can we allow ourselves to acknowledge the good that we do and what sustains us in our profession? This question is further developed in our next chapter focusing on the spirituality of caregiving called "Spirituality: The Sinew of our Human Experience."

Timeout: A Moment of Reprieve

At your own pace, give yourself a moment of leisure to reflect on each question below.

1. What is your understanding of reflection? Can you recognize when you are doing it?

2. What insights inspired you in reading through the different vignettes in this chapter?

3. Is reflection a practice that is helpful to you?

4. Do you recognize an ending, a journey, and a new beginning that has happened or is now happening to you? Can you recall an event that was transformative and a real game changer for you?

5. Did the discussion about the symptoms of PTSD help you to discover how PTSD is not a mental illness?

Chapter 8 - Spirituality, the Sinew of our Human Experience

Introduction

There is nothing objective about spirituality. There may be different shades of gray to its meaning. For some, it is an energizing search for meaning. Others are simply repulsed when spirituality is mentioned, as memories of painful experiences emerge from their past. Still, others are repulsed by the news or experience of the fundamental fringes that often seem alive and well within many spiritual and religious traditions. Others simply reject anything spiritual. In general, caregivers are trained to remain neutral, that is, to be hospitable to the spiritual traditions of those they are called to serve. Often, sensitivity to these beliefs helps in building trust, as many studies have shown, a person's spirituality aids in the healing process. In this chapter, I want to introduce the premise that there is a spirituality of caregiving, something that resides deep within the Soul of the caregiver.

Enfleshed Spirituality

The miracle of spirituality is enfleshed in who we are as humankind. Believer and nonbeliever, churched and unchurched, agnostic and atheist, humanist and theist, we all share a common spirituality, we are human. The sinew, the fibers that hold muscle to bone, is similar to the balance between flesh and spirit. In this balance of creation, the living principle that permeates our flesh is spiritual, like the air we breathe. The key word is enfleshed, which means the physical is infused with a living energy we can call spirit. Flesh becomes enlivened as depicted by the stunning, serene, yet dramatic fresco of Michelangelo's interpretation of the Genesis creation story in the Sistine Chapel. Imagine the yearning of Adam, seeking to discover the sacred within him, reaching out, gazing forward with eyes fixed on the One he is to encounter, extending a hand to be grasped by God. You can feel Adam, eager and receptive, to touch the hand of God. In that synapse between them, that space that is as close as it is distant, life occurs, matter and spirit are joined. Their extended hands become a metaphor for a deeper willingness to share life.

Hands as a Metaphor

Pause for a moment to gaze at your hands. Notice how alive they are. Life pulsates through veins and arteries, feeding cells and exchanging nutrients for metabolized wastes. Structurally held together by bone and sinew, hands feel warm, sometimes cold, and made able to move by millions of electrically-charged neurons. These hands show the fruits of their labors, some with the calluses and bruises of farmers and laborers, others cared for as those of a surgeon, therapist, or nurse, others delicate and fashionable as the principal ballet dancer or violin player, still others with the strength to reach out in friendship with the shake of a hand. Hands whirl flour-dusted pizza dough into the air, create, tailor, and mend our garments and cook, holding up a wooden spoon to taste a simmering soup.

Hands can both hold one tenderly in an embrace, reassuring, caressing, and making love. God is personified and holds us in the palm of his hands in Hebrew and Christian scriptures. At other times they protect, push away, creating personal boundaries and are ready for self-defense, and can punish. Hands can be raised in protest, as in a march or joined together in moments of gratitude, welcoming, and prayer. They clap following experiences and performances of excellence. Hands can be young and not so young, male and female, some with painted nails and some with broken nails. Others are natural with different hues of color depicting the cultural diversity of humanity that reminds us not only of the life within them, but also the lives they represent.

Each hand is alive because of the spirit of life that animates each of them. Spirit, or some may say Soul, is the vital animating essence of a person, animal and plant, tree and vegetation as believed in many spiritual traditions, such as Father Sky and Mother Earth. Spirit is about the non-physical, about the Soul. This broader understanding enables us to imagine spirituality as it relates to this animating energy or force within a person. Spirituality is multi-faceted like the hues of a precious gem with varying degrees of understanding. Spirituality is about life. It is about living. It is about one's relationship to self, about one's relationship to others and about one's relationship to the Holy Other, the All One. Houston Smith speaks about this trinity of relationships and how they are related.[104] For example, if we focus on the transcendent Other, the All One, we will also discover something about ourselves and creation. We may begin our reflection on the beauty of creation, or on our friends or family and in doing so, we may experience the transcendent Other. Likewise, if we begin to reflect on the miracle of who we are, our real selves as Jung would like to call it, it is in this reflection we will discover not only something about ourselves, but also something about creation, others, and the Other.

Spirituality is the living principle, the sinew of our human experience. This living principle, the energy that makes us alive, circulates throughout the flesh of our hands. Life lives within us and outside of us, in the world we inhabit, from the heights of the heavens to the depths of the seas to the hills and valleys of the earth. Fruits of the earth, golden waves of planted grains, and dew drenched forests share a common bond with us. So too, do the creatures of the seas, birds of the air and creatures of the land breathe the spirit of creation. Each in their own way reminds us that we share with creation the miracle of life. Caregivers sustain life for those they serve, struggling to rescue and protect and at the same time very much aware that there is a circle of life. Just as there is a beginning when one is born, there is also an ending when one's life changes at death.

Caregivers Know the Difference

We, as caregivers, know when someone is not alive. When we caress the hand of a grandparent who has just died. We know just as clearly as a surgeon does when a heart stops during surgery and cannot be resuscitated. The life that once circulated and gave color and warmth has left. We also know the pain of burying our pet cat or dog in the backyard, or the goldfish that just didn't survive from our own experiences or those of our children or grandchildren. We are aware that the first frost that beautifies and blankets the land with a delicate white will kill flowers or damage crops. Seasons mark this change as the circle of life continues.

Caregivers face the drama of life and death each day, such as the miracle and joy of delivering a newborn baby, as well as the tragedy and pain of a stillborn child. The satisfaction of saving a life in the emergency room animates the staff and carries them through the sadness when a clinician pronounces someone dead on arrival. The hospice nurse reaches out to a questioning spouse who wonders if life has left and becomes the midwife, tenderly taking the hand of a spouse or friend to comfort when their loved one has died. The parents who, day in and day out, selflessly care for their child with cerebral palsy, celebrating each milestone of achievement, grieve just as deeply as parents who suffer over the premature death of a child, a victim of an opium overdose.

Paramedics and first responders also know the difference between life and death in facing the tragedies of traffic accidents, searching for the victims of floods, wildfires, or hurricanes. They experience the joy of a rescue and the pain of not finding survivors. Their rapid response teams practice and are on alert, ever questioning whether or not they could have done better. Their debriefing sessions support each other in the recognition that it is difficult to bear human tragedies that leave no one unscathed. What and who sustains these courageous men and women in their service as caregivers? Is it their call to service that both energizes them and also sustains them through traumatic events? They, like most caregivers, would agree that something greater than themselves sustains them, yet few would recognize or call what they do so selflessly, a spiritual practice. Is it possible now to entertain and suggest that this energizing and animating spirit of one's call to service might also be called spirituality?

Is the work that we caregivers do just a job or is it a calling, and as such, is the caregiving that we do a spiritual practice? We are not going to church, or synagogue, or to a mosque or to a monastery or to an ashram, nor are we going to our prayer circle or gathering in the wilderness. We don't need our bible, rosary beads, prayer shawl, or chants that may be used afterwards. Our journey is an interior one, where spirit and flesh meet. It is at this juncture, similar to many of the different spiritual and religious creation myths of humankind that the recollection of an experience, of an image that seeks a voice, gains insight. Imagine this life-giving force circulating throughout your body sustaining you as a caregiver.

Holding What Cannot Be Held

How does one hold what seems to be unbearable for both caregivers and those being served? Consider the experience of Chaplain Richards, a seasoned member of the interdisciplinary team at a trauma one medical center who, like the director of a one-act tragedy, was called to the emergency room. Mr. Brown was on his way to the hospital because he had suffered a massive cardiac arrest at home. He was an elder at the First Baptist Church in his community, and members of his family sang in the choir. He was the glue that held his large African-American extended family together. He and his family were celebrating the birthday of one of their grandchildren, laughing and playing games, all in a festive mood when suddenly Mr. Brown fell to the floor. One of his daughters who was an RN rushed to his side and began cardiopulmonary resuscitation (CPR), while his son called 911. His wife, trying to keep her composure, escorted the children to another room. Within minutes, the paramedics took over, continuing CPR, taking vital signs, communicating with the ER physician, starting an IV and administering cardiac medications. The call to service was immediate for Chaplain Richards, the ER physician, and the paramedics. Still doing CPR on arrival, the emergency room staff continued to no avail, and he was pronounced dead shortly after his arrival.

Most of the family of Mr. Brown followed the ambulance to the emergency room, while a daughter remained at home with the children. They were greeted by Chaplain Richards who led them to the ER family room. He had already been informed of the situation by the ER staff. Their panic and apprehension were increased as they wondered why a chaplain would greet them. Years of training prepared Chaplain Richards to face such situations. Calmly, he reassured the family that this was the protocol of the hospital in emergency situations, and the doctor had asked him to help get the family settled until he could come and speak with them. He told them that they were still doing CPR and that the situation was very serious. "Is he going to live?" shouted one of his daughters? A prediction only the doctor could confirm, a decision that Chaplin Richards was gently preparing the family to hear. "It is very grave," he replied. Tearfully, she mentioned that on the way to the hospital, her mother called their pastor and he too, was on his way.

Clearly, the family was in shock, tearful and anxious, now experiencing for the first time, the fact that the patriarch and elder of their family, a spouse, a father, and grandfather may die. How does one hold what no one wants to acknowledge? Would their spirituality support them and be a resource to them? Within this tension of holding the tragedy and the suffering and woundedness, is there a possibility of discovering healing and transformation, something of what Arthur Egendorf suggests evokes at least symbolic death and new awareness.[105] One's response to trauma or woundedness gradually leads to this letting go, a sort of dying and rising or what we discussed earlier by William Bridges, an ending, the uncertainties, and a new beginning. This was the process that would face the Brown family.

Facing the ending of a loved one's life, what seems worse than death, may become in time, life-giving and transformative. Holding what appears to be unbearable, feeling the pain that has no end, walking into the depths of one's netherworld, allowing the darkness to surround one, are stepping stones in the process of descent. Each is able to bear the pain and find his or her own way through the labyrinth of the Soul in seeking transformation. This was the certitude Chaplain Richards experienced as he witnessed the pain and trauma of the Brown family entering into this mystery, not only of their husband and father dying, but something also in them that was being transformed.

Chaplain Richards reassured the family that he would keep them informed as he went to check with the doctor who had already pronounced Mr. Brown dead. The doctor asked if he should now come and speak with the family. Chaplain Richards suggested he wait until Mr. Brown's pastor arrives, due to the family's need for support and their strong spiritual ties with their Church, as well as their fear of his possible death. Just then, the pastor arrived and was met by Chaplin Richards who briefed him on the doctor's findings and escorted him to the family conference room.

As soon as Pastor Williams entered the room, there was an outburst of emotion. He shared with the family how grave he believed the situation was and led them in prayer for strength. It was then the doctor arrived and compassionately told the family that Mr. Brown had essentially died at home due to a traumatic cardiac arrest. He expressed his condolences and left the room. In the meantime, the nurses were preparing Mr. Brown to be seen by his family. Pastor Williams embraced Mrs. Brown, who began weeping uncontrollably as her glistening tears streamed through the aged wrinkles of her mahogany completion. Each of the children surrounded their mother in a circle of compassion and grief. Ernie, the oldest of the five children, recognized his new role to support his mother and other siblings, and he asked what was next.

Chaplain Richards asked if anyone in the family would like to see Mr. Brown and he would escort them, a few at a time, into the ER proper. Afterwards, Mr. Brown would be taken to the hospital morgue until the funeral director was chosen. Papers needed to be signed, giving permission for the hospital to release the remains to the funeral director who would be in touch with the family. Each person involved had a reliance on and support from a different understanding of spirituality that sustained them during this traumatic event. The paramedics, the doctor, the chaplain, the ER staff, the pastor, and the family each held on, sometimes blindly, sometimes unnerved, and sometimes with a steel and steadfast faith, because of their spiritual roots and their spirituality. So, what then, is spirituality?

The Many Facets of Spirituality

While spirituality is often equated with a formalized religious practice, with deities, gods and goddesses, the supernatural, the afterlife, and religious traditions and practices, its essence lies at the center of being human. Spirituality is as natural as one's breathing. Many spiritual traditions incorporate a practice of breathing in their spiritual rituals. Spirituality may also find its expression in nature, humanism, psychology, philosophy, the arts, and religious practice. Breathing in and breathing out is a conscious and unconscious rhythm of uniting, at the center of one's being, the elements of the earth with the elements of the sky, the arena of life where physical and spirit meet. Breathing in and breathing out is humankind's universal experience of common ground, awareness of being one with the All One and one with all beings and creation.

As there is movement in the exercise of breathing, so too is spirituality an animating force of change and movement within a person.[106] As such, our call to action as caregivers is often guided by those spiritual values within us, or what I like to call a spirituality of caregiving. Breathing in and breathing out restores wellness and hope, of catching one's breath, accepting the gift of life giving air within the deepest caverns of one's Soul. Spirit enters and is united with one's spirit and in doing so, energizes one. To breath out, to exhale is a metaphor of spiriting one to serve those in need. Healers of body, mind and spirit breath unites each caregiver with the human drama of illness and wellness, suffering, and comfort in being at ease with both the miracles and limitations of caregiving.

From a Depth-Psychological Perspective

Understanding spirituality as a natural urge within a person was developed in the writings of the psychoanalysts Sigmund Freud and C.G. Jung. These natural urges are not tangible, not in the sky, not in the supernatural, but in the natural essence of being human. As mentioned earlier, being human is to be enfleshed, that is matter and spirit are united. This is difficult for us Westerners raised in a culture that separates the logos and mythos of the human experience from each other. This is not to say that in reality they are united, it simply means it is in the human experience, in the boundaries that contain who I am, that I am most myself and that I can and do experience transcendence. This is why I so marvel at the insight of Joseph Campbell that was quoted earlier when one of his students asked, "Where is heaven?"[107]

Let's explore substituting heaven for the "sacred," or "Holy Other," or "spirituality." Campbell continues: "It is above? Then the birds will be there before you. Is it below? Then the fish will be there before you. The Kingdom of God is within you. Who and what is in Heaven? God is in Heaven. Where is God? Within you!"[108] Eastern spiritualities start with this premise of humanity and spiritual experience. We in the west go through the back door to arrive at the same conclusion. How often, in the Christian Tradition we recall Jesus saying, "The kingdom of God is within you."

Suspended between inner and outer, earth and sky, what is above and below, resides that meeting place where gods and goddesses, humankind, and the mysteries of the universe become one. "Thou art That!" articulates as well as it can, that unity where the Divine, whom the individual desires, resides not only within that individual but is identical with a universal, absolute consciousness of the sacred. This meeting point or threshold is the language of metaphor and is where mystics roam and see reality differently. Metaphor, like the discipline of prayer, becomes the portal by which the seeker journeys beyond the historical fact to an experience that transcends one's human experience. Lionel Corbett also articulates this experience: "This non-dual notion of the Self expresses in psychological language the mystical understanding that, in Eckert's words, 'my me is God, or as the Upanishads of the Hindu myths put it, 'thou art that.'"[109]

The experience is not outside ourselves but within. Here are examples of what I mean. If I were raised in the western culture derived from the Greek and Roman influences, I would probably consider the sacred outside of myself. There is me and there is the sacred other.

Freud was averse to using the term "spiritual" as he equated it to religion. Again, wanting to stress the normalness of humanity that he found in these spiritual urges, he used the German term '*stelle*'. Translated, it means an embodied Soul that contains within it all the natural instincts needed for one's selfactualization,[110] a process of clarifying who we are destined to be. Could we argue that his understanding of the interior process is spiritual, as is our own natural spirituality, just as we understand the naturalness of flesh and spirit in our hands?

Jung also realized that this natural urge and the psychic energies of a person are intrinsic to being human. He called this the process of individuation, a process of a person discovering his or her true self, which involves both an individual and the collective unconscious. Unlike Freud, he suggests that within this natural urge, there is also a transcendent quality that leads one to reflect beyond oneself. This led Jung to define spirituality as the "careful and scrupulous observation of the numinosum."[111] Gaining insight from our reflections is something we do every day. It is in the midst of these reflections that one may experience the sacred. For example, as we witness the sun rising over the hills and valleys or setting of the sun into the Pacific, within this experience, we may gain insight into God or the Holy Other as creator of this panorama of color. In doing so, almost without any effort, we experience what Jung called, the numinosum, which simply means the presence of a divinity, something spiritual, something awe-inspiring. In particular, Jung understood numinosity in the context of archetypes that are universal patterns and are an attitude of instinct. Caregiving is an example of a pattern of behavior that influences the work that we do with a certain attitude, or I would suggest, calling.

A Caregiver's Spirituality

Caregivers have these qualities and are influenced by values that often change how they view their calling. Recall how those in the healing professions live out the archetypes of the wounded healer, the caregiver, or the hero, to name a few. Each profession has their own unique culture and archetype that reminds them that they belong to something bigger than their individual self. What does it mean to be a police officer, or a detective belonging to a fraternal order of police committed to living out the pledge of the "Blue Line," a line separating what is good from those activities that are not? The collective consciousness of the group encompasses values and beliefs that support and encourage its members in their search for meaning.

Another definition of spirituality that caregivers experience is one suggested by Robert Grant. Spirituality "is grounded in the ability to foster relationship, to be connected, and to be whole. Wholeness requires embracing dimensions of inner and outer reality that life outside has been 'taken for granted."[112] The very act of caregiving is relational, a meeting between the caregiver and the one being served, as well as one's relationship to the event and how it affects oneself. There is always the tension of applying one's professional and technical skills to a situation, as well as the relationship one has with the one being served, about the team members, and about one's own relationship with one's self.

Discovering and understanding the different movements of his Soul, let alone following through on them was new for Dusty, a nickname for Duston. As a vice-president of Human Resources, he discovered too late and not so lately, how he took for granted the importance of relationships and in particular, how he dismissed the relationship he had with himself, his family, and the spiritual inheritance he learned as the son of a Congregational minister.

The Son of a Preacher Man

As early as Dusty can remember, he was always a caregiver. Inspired by his father, who was pastor of a progressive nondenominational Congregational Church. Dusty would tag along with his parents, brother, and sister at each church function. As he grew older, he volunteered to help out with different outreach programs in the community. He felt a particular sensitivity and compassion for the underserved. He enjoyed serving meals in the church soup kitchen, as well as belonging to the youth group who went on missions to poorer areas of the country. It would be years later that he realized this sensitivity was borne out of his own unconscious need to care for himself, something he did not learn at home. There is a positive and shadow side to caregiving. Often an obsessive need to help others and at other times to wear masks that deaden the cry of one's own Soul pain.

What he couldn't reconcile nor understand was his parent's use of recreational drugs. It just didn't make sense to Dusty, as they both were well-respected leaders in the community and known for their empathy and pastoral concern. This quandary would eventually lead him to leave the Church. What was missing in each of their lives and more importantly, what was Dusty missing in his? His father was the pastor and each time before a service he would smoke some weed. He later learned that his grandfather would die of cirrhosis of the liver due to alcoholism, and it would be years later, when confronted with his own addiction, that Dusty could link the intergenerational pattern of addictive behaviors within his family of origin. He learned that addictive behaviors mask one's real need to form relationships. Caregiving, while enriching in itself, had its shadow side. These pitfalls reveal themselves in being a martyr and not being able to say no. Enabling others at one's own expense, being codependent, and feeling guilty that you have not accomplished enough are other pitfalls.

A Professional Juggler

Dusty, in his new position as VP of HR for a large telecommunications company, found himself assuming a variety of roles with the different associates who came to his office. One day, he found himself consoling an associate whose husband was killed in an auto accident. Another day, he listened to a disgruntled director having a bad hair day. Still another, he worked with his team organizing the annual employee picnic. He enjoyed this aspect of his job as an informal social worker, pastoral counselor, and financial advisor, always having one or two balls in the air, as he prided himself on being a juggler. Long hours, however, began to take a toll on him, as well as the unending organizational demands as the Vice President of Human Resources. He got the nickname "Dusty" early on because of his golden-brown hair, but in a way, he enjoyed being the 'dust mop' of the organization, cleaning up other people's' issues.

To keep himself going, he would have two or three martinis at the end of each day. Little did he recognize that he had inherited the addictive behaviors of his parents. In one of his college courses, he had to do a genogram, which is similar to doing a family tree. The focus, however, is on the emotional, social, spiritual, and psychological issues of his family. What he learned but didn't take to heart was that he could trace addictive behaviors not only in his parents, but to five past generations. There was also a pattern of the men in the family dying early, and the anger and resentment of their wives forced to go it alone. He learned that there was a strong reliance on faith. Not only was his father a pastor, but also his father's father. The question then arose for Dusty, what was missing in each of their lives, and now even in his own? Why didn't their spiritual practice support them in this process? This was the reason, as an adult, he left formalized religious practice to seek an answer.

Blessings and Pitfalls

While one can focus on the strengths of a caregiver, the caregiver also can fall victim to what Carol S Pearson calls pitfalls.[113] Dusty was well known in the company for his compassion and being one whose door was always open. As best he could, he tried to model the leadership qualities of servant leadership as outlined by Robert Greenfield.[114] His duties as an HR executive made him an advocate both for the associates who sought his help and at the executive table where he helped promote policies for them. What Dusty didn't recognize were the pitfalls he would stumble into that developed from his generous heart. He often felt overwhelmed, going in so many directions, unable to say no to demands from the executive leadership office and the demands from the associates. He often felt like a martyr for the cause, sword in hand and ready for the battle cry.

Codependency and enabling others are behaviors inherent in addictive personalities which he also recognized. It is as ludicrous as his hosting a cocktail party in honor of his partner celebrating sobriety. He learned early that he should not upset the applecart at home. If one member of a household takes the risk of self-improvement and growth, the family system is affected, and the resistance of the other family members builds, often to sabotage the one seeking recovery.

If one takes on too much, maybe trying to fill a personal interior void, then one has little time for self-care. If one never feels good enough, then it is possible not to set healthy boundaries. Resentment and guilt can build up, creating craving for a good old fashioned "pity party." However, this does not undermine the core values and qualities of the caregiver such as nurturance, compassion, dedication, generosity, service, and personal sacrifice for the good of others. The qualities of being supportive, kind, helpful, altruistic, caring, and concerned with the well-being of others are still core competencies and skills.[115] Dusty discovered he exhibited all the pitfalls listed above, in particular being the martyr and lacking in self-care. If only he cared enough, if only he had done more. "If only" became his mantra until one day he ran out of gas. He became a caretaker instead of a caregiver, and the emptiness he experienced was filled with alcohol.

A Balm in Gilead

In his search for answers, Dusty came to the awareness that he was an alcoholic which became his "Balm in Gilead," a mantra of an African-American Spiritual he remembered when he was in the youth group at this father's church. However, he realized that he was substituting alcohol for a deeper opportunity for self-awareness and relationship building. Intuitively, Dusty was searching for meaning and healing that he did not find being the son of a preacher-man. The route he took, the balm he sought, the tonic he thought would refresh him, did not heal, as living on the surface of things did not address his real Soul pain that was being drowned with alcohol. He yearned for what the spiritual promised:

> "There is a Balm in Gilead that makes the wounded whole.
> There is a Balm in Gilead that heals the sin-sick Soul."[116]

It is often said, that while a person may leave a particular spiritual practice, such as going to church, mosque, meeting room, or synagogue, that the person's spirituality continues to reside deep within his or her consciousness, always having the potential for deeper and richer growth. This consciousness hit Dusty like a thunderbolt one day at work. It had become clear that he needed to write his resignation letter and resign. Years of caregiving had taken their toll, with little or no time for self-care. He was suffering from compassion fatigue leading to burnout - which will be explored further in Chapter Ten. Patricia Smith argues that compassion fatigue occurs when one neglects self-care that addresses physical, psychological, interpersonal, and spiritual needs that help one cope with the stress of caregiving.[117] Dusty would often say to himself, "There is so much to be done!" which of course led him to disregard his own needs for self-care. There was, however, a flicker of hope that Dusty felt, and it was on the strength of this experience that he went to see Dan White, a pastoral counselor specializing in addiction, whom he had met earlier at an HR conference. He was impressed with Dan's sincerity and his informal invitation to call him if he ever needed help.

After a month of visiting Dan three times a week, he asked him, "how long will it take to get back on my feet." There was a pause, and then Dan's gentle response. "Dusty, it's not a matter of Zap, Bam, Alakazam, and you drink another tonic. It's about facing a new normal, a new lifestyle, a new recognition that you are now on a journey of healing that will continue for the rest of your life." Dusty nodded in agreement, feeling somewhat relieved, as Dan just verified what Dusty was intuitively feeling, that he could rely on his spiritual strengths, which had become an integral part of Dusty's DNA. At the root of many addictive behaviors is fear of building relationships. Dusty now discovered in trusting Dan, he was also discovering and recovering the relationship he so desired with himself.

Relationships and Spirituality

Spirituality encompasses an awareness of relationships with all creation, as well as an appreciation of presence and purpose that includes a sense of meaning. A divine presence dwells intimately in the world of creation, which carries a refinement of emotion and sensitivity caused by the delicacy, fragrance, indescribable beauty, and rhythmic movement of the world, argues Thomas Berry.[118] Art, poetry, music, literature, dance, theater, and life's experiences may lead one to reflect, to contemplate, and embrace a mystical sensibility. Mysticism is not reserved for saints, shamans and sages alone. Neither is mysticism outside the realm of the ordinary.

The question becomes: As a caregiver, am I aware that I participate in many different and unique relationships with my clients, myself, and the sacred. The Hindu revelation that you are it or "Thou Art That" led Joseph Campbell to the awareness that the gods are a projection of one's own inner fire. "Follow the footsteps to your center and know that from within you, gods are born. The deities are symbolic personifications of the energy that you are yourself. Within you is where the gods dwell."[119] The reverential salutation "Namaste" found in many different Hindu and Asian traditions articulates this profound truth, that the I who greets you, bows to the divine in you.[120]

"Thou Art That" articulates as well as it can, that unity where the Divine, the sacred, the hero's quest, that the individual desires, resides not only within that individual, but is identical to a universal consciousness of the sacred. This meeting point or threshold can only be described in the language of metaphor. In this space is also where we can roam and see reality differently. Campbell discovered, through his research, travels and reflection, a universal unity between the myths of the world. He found it possible for one to see beyond all the facts, questions, and boundaries to the vitalizing energy that the symbol or myth signifies.[121] This is the latent energy we possess as caregivers.

Spirituality and Transcendence

Transcendence is a human activity that takes one outside oneself as an active participant in the everyday moments and experiences of life. The art of contemplation may open one up to mystery and a process of reflection that instantly moves one out of an "either/or" box. Sages, tricksters, mystics, priests, rabbis and shamans experience the sacred and mirror this experience from an insider's view. Ordinary reflection opens up the possibility of contemplative reflection. This process of exploration and reflection becomes a transformative act, allowing one to experience the sacred. An experience of the sacred is borne out of one's human experience. The task for the caregiver is to give him or herself permission to allow these insights to develop and percolate.

Bernini's sculpture of the "Rapture of St. Theresa" in Santa Maria Victoria Church in Rome invites the viewer to enter into the artist's vision of how marble can reflect human experience. One wonders what drew Bernini to enliven marble with what he experienced within himself. What was stirring in his Soul, as he got lost in that moment in time, when eternity opened up before him? A moment outside the constraints of time and space captivated Bernini and fueled his struggle to articulate one raptured in love. Within the ordinary and within this liminal meeting place, opens the possibility of transcendence for us, the viewers. As dramatic as this work of art is to us as participants in this encounter, are there not stories that need to be carved from within us, experiences that need to be shared, insights developed, and wisdom revealed that support and sustain us as caregivers?

Reflection allows caregivers to see beyond and through the symbol and image of our experiences. We discover in a flash the curtain of uncertainties that separates one from the sacred that is lifted by these insights. One who was once outside, is now inside this sacred sanctuary as outer and inner merge. What appeared distant and unclear melts within the radiance of the present moment. Barriers that once separated mortals from gods are shattered in the numinosity of the experience. The experiences of mystics and spiritual leaders remind us that we too, share in this human experience of reflection that allows us to see and understand, in the silence of our being, where time and space disappear.

The field of comparative religion is born out of the tension of different views. Religion becomes another view or lens to use in understanding the transcendent function of a people and a culture. An observation about a particular faith tradition by an anthropologist, psychologist, mythologist, or comparative religionist is an outsider's view, in that they do not practice or participate in the mythos of that faith tradition. Sensitivity to an insider view does add a unique and powerful view. Paden writes that "much more specific to religion than cognitive representation is the participatory character of meanings and symbols."[122] These symbols also transform perception and in doing so engage the participant. Such was the experience of Maria, who despite relying on her faith, found herself fearful and anxious over her open-heart surgery. As she was being prepared for surgery, she asked the nurse if she could see the chaplain. Conscious of the importance of a patient's well-being and how this contributes to the overall successful outcome of the surgery, the nurse reassured Maria and called the chaplain. Maria was to discover how much she was a participant in her own recovery.

Caught in the Cauldron of Anxiety and Fear

Sinking in a cauldron of anxiety and fear, a patient questions the resources of her faith to seek support and guidance. Experiencing emotional and spiritual stress over her upcoming open-heart surgery, she relied on her faith and prayers to assist her, but to no avail. She became more anxious and asked the nurse to call the chaplain for support. Maria, a seventy-year-old woman of the Roman Catholic faith, specifically asked for a priest. After the normal introductions, Maria greeted the chaplain with the words: "I am praying to God that I will not be anxious about the surgery, yet I am still anxious." Struggling to use her faith and interior resources to cope with her anxiety, she found herself falling down a spiral descent of no return, so powerful that she even considered postponing the surgery.

While exploring Maria's particular anxieties about the surgery, such as pain management, what the doctor and nurses had previously told her, her length of stay, some possible complications, and even her fear of dying, the chaplain asked almost matter-of-factly: "Did you ever consider just telling God you were anxious?" Maria looked at the chaplain with amazement. That she could actually tell God what she was feeling was a new insight for her. Calm came over Maria, as the suggestion that a deity could possibly understand her feelings, shattered her image of a distant god.

Allowing this new image of God to speak on its own terms became a process of transformation and healing for Maria from a distant God. A God for whom she had to struggle to get things right, to an image of God as faithful, loving, compassionate, and merciful. God is portrayed as a Divine Lover in the Song of Songs within the Hebrew Scriptures. Within the Christian tradition, images of a God "who so loved the world" emerge in the Gospel of John. Similarly, within the Sufi tradition of Islam, God is imaged as the Beloved.

Anxiety about open-heart surgery is certainly normal and to be expected, yet Maria's own demons tied her up in knots. In the midst of them, she knew she could rely on the wisdom that emerged in her relationship with the chaplain. A spiritual guide had appeared in the person of the chaplain and a restoration of her faith led her to put her anxieties in perspective. The sacrament of the sick was administered, and the chaplain accompanied her to the doors of the surgery suite. When she woke up in intensive care after surgery, the chaplain was there doing his rounds. As he approached and took her hand, she smiled, squeezed his hand, and simply said, "Thank you."

The lesson Maria learned during her hospital stay was that the supernatural is not outside human experience. Understanding the transcendent as a supernatural phenomenon is only possible, if understood from this human perspective. Religion and religious practice then become an expression of one's natural, innate spirituality. Jung believed that since God is an archetype, He already has a place in the deepest center of our psyche that is preexistent to consciousness. "We neither make Him more remote nor eliminate Him but bring Him closer to the possibility of being experienced."[123] It is often during and after the experience of a traumatic event, that one has the opportunity to discover how and when the sacred can be experienced. This is the challenge for caregivers and for those we are called to serve.

Trauma as Soul Building

When one experiences a traumatic event, the impact of the event is seared within the caregiver's Soul and has a conscious and unconscious effect. Some experiences may be so serious that they leave one almost paralyzed with fear and the possibility of a traumatic event continually recurring. Some caregivers just push the experience aside and get on to the next task at hand. Trauma may also resurface old patterns of trauma that were hidden, those traumas experienced as a child, or later on in life, that suddenly appear, almost to haunt one, always seeking a voice to be heard. Other traumas may awaken in the caregiver one morning, and the subsequent emotional outburst helps the caregiver realize the depth of suffering from an accumulation of traumatic events. The pain of one's Soul is finally heard and has had enough, as each aching fiber of the Soul pain one experiences becomes a guide to seeking appropriate help.

Robert Grant defines "trauma" as "an overwhelming life event(s) that renders most people powerless and/or living in fear of their life. The major challenge of trauma is to integrate its impact into personal and collective frames of meaning."[124] The task or challenge, suggests Grant, is to find meaning in afflictions. Jung believes this is one of the functions of the psyche. In allowing the experience of pain to be felt, one may experience wisdom that is hidden within, maintaining that "Tears, sorrow, and disappointment are bitter, but wisdom is the comforter in all psychic suffering.[125] As Hillman suggests, "Afflictions point to gods; gods reach us through afflictions"[126] "Compared to the finite nature of the traumatized Soul," writes Greg Mogenson "the traumatic event seems infinite, all-powerful, and wholly other"[127] Herein lies the dilemma that Mogenson presents. On the one hand, suffering and traumatic events encase and close one off to allowing the events to be experienced personally. On the other hand, Mogenson concludes that only when the trauma is felt through a dying and rising experience, like a grain of sand forming into a pearl, does one enter into the process of Soul-making.[128]

The Spirituality of Caregiving

Our discussion of spirituality throughout this chapter has taken us on a journey of discovering that goals, aspirations, commitment, passion, values, and the dedication we share as caregivers are steeped in a spirituality of caregiving. Just as the air we breathe is a metaphor for welcoming the sacred or divine host into the core of our being through the gentle act of inhalation, so too, because of this sacred encounter and interchange, we are sent out in the service of others by the act of exhaling. The ancient exhortation and dismissal from the Catholic Mass, "Ite missa est" says it best, as you have experienced healing transformation during this sacred ritual, so go forth and serve others. Breathing in and out is a simple example of the interchange between flesh and spirit, between a sacred encounter and the commission to serve those in need. We are fed emotionally and spiritually when we do the work of caregiving.

The question I asked in an earlier chapter and one that I always ask at the beginning of any lecture or workshop I give is: "Are you a better person because of your work as a caregiver? Most agree and nod their heads yes and then move onto the next call or the next patient. The real question is: "Are we, as caregivers, open to the transformative possibilities that occur because of the work that we do?" Our work is value driven. Our work is interior, as we listen to those interior movements of our Soul. Just as we are fed by this reflective process and experience a sense of spirituality at it foundational roots, so too, do we have the privilege to drink from the fountain of caregiving. This feeding, or tending to our Soul, nourishes us in the careers that do make us whole. The work that we do is a spiritual practice.

One such person who has committed her entire career to study, research, and support in advocating the importance of spirituality in healthcare is Dr. Christina Puchalski, founder and director of George Washington Institute of Spirituality and Health (GWISH.) The Institute stresses the importance of recognizing the spiritual dimension of health and suffering. She argues that spirituality is the dimension of a person that seeks to find meaning in his or her life, and that spirituality is also the quality that supports connection to and relationship with the sacred, as well as with one another. If this is so, how does the work we do build a connection to and a relationship with the one we serve? Our discussion earlier that we are wounded healers gives us pause to understand that the very act of caregiving is how we integrate spirituality in the work that we do.

Puchalski believes that as physicians and healthcare workers become more aware of the importance of the spiritual needs of those who are ill and suffering, it will lead them to more compassionate care. Interaction of physicians, nurses, chaplains, social workers, therapists and auxiliary support personnel with those who are ill, demands self-sacrifice and compassion. Such interactions become a spiritual practice. Herein lies the underlying thesis of this work: While caregivers are trained to recognize the spiritual needs of those they serve, caregivers also discover, participate in, and are animated by their spirituality of caregiving.

Spirituality is an important resource when one experiences different traumatic events in life. The integration of spirituality, caregiving and health is an ancient practice that continues to motivate educators of healthcare today. In a task force called *Spirituality, Culture and End of Life Care*, Puchalski and her colleagues made recommendations that were included in *Report III, Contemporary Issues in Medicine: Communication in Medicine* of the Medical School Objective Project (MSOP). The report recognized the importance and necessity of the physician developing communication skills in supporting and facilitating a conversation about a patient's spirituality.[129]

Spirituality is recognized as a factor that contributes to the health and healing of many individuals. Recognizing that spirituality is found in all cultures and societies, the following is a consensus definition. The report states that spirituality is recognized as a factor that contributes to health in many persons, and spirituality is found in all cultures and societies. It is expressed in an individual's search for ultimate meaning through participation in religion and/or belief in God, family, naturalism, rationalism, humanism and the arts. It is important to note that each of these factors can influence how patients and healthcare professionals perceive health and illness, as well as how they interact with one another.[130] The question that remains for me is: "How do we, as caregivers, discover the spirituality that is truly our own?" We don't have to look outside ourselves, to the heavens or the depths below. What we so desire, a spirituality that supports and sustains us, is within us. The secret or the key that unlocks this mystery is within our power to unfold. It is a matter of allowing the stirrings of our Soul to be heard. It's about developing a spiritual practice.

In our next chapter, "Practice, Practice, Practice" I want to explore what a spiritual practice is and how caregiving is such a practice. Think for a moment, especially when we are distracted by family or world events, how we have to create the space and be hospitable enough to welcome the client or the patient. These actions are heroic examples of how caregiving is a spiritual practice. The ordinary becomes spiritual as we discover, through our journey, the interior strengths and values that give birth to meaning, insight, and transformation.

Timeout: A Moment of Reprieve

Time to catch our breath. If you feel you are standing on your head, and that your worldview about spirituality is in transition, or that you are ready to scream, wonderful! You are at a good place. Allow what is stirring have a voice. Here are some questions to ponder. Take your time, this is NOT a test. It is about you and what you have learned about listening to the stirrings of your Soul.

1. You belong to a noble profession. How has reading through this chapter assisted you in more appreciating the work that you do?

2. Were you able to gain insight from the different stories presented in this chapter? Can you identify with any of the characters?

3. How has the discussion about trauma and traumatic events helped you to realize that you are not alone in experiencing these events as a caregiver?

Chapter 9 - Practice! Practice! Practice!

Introduction

Practice! Time for Practice. How often has this word conjured up both excitement and resistance within us? Practice is embedded in our genes seeking to bring to fruition what lies dormant within us. Conscious and unconscious stirrings both from interior or exterior promptings motivate us to excel, to move forward, and to succeed. From our earliest years, from the exuberance of taking our first stumbling steps to the joys of learning or memorizing the alphabet, to learning both the constraints, as well as the rewards of parental guidance.

Practice helps to make us feel more confident in what we are doing. How many arguments did we have or continually have with parents, coaches, instructors, and professors about the importance of practice, especially when we were the least motivated? The concert pianist didn't just appear on the stage, dropping down from the heavens playing on celestial keys, but spent many long and tedious hours of practice to sharpen his or her skills. Likewise, those that are fortunate enough to make the Olympic Teams, do so because of hours and hours of sometimes tedious, yet committed practice. A spark within these aspirants guides them to become Olympic Champions.

We, of lesser fame may need more time to learn the musical scales, even when at times we wonder why we chose to play flute in the first place. What about all those extra push-ups we did in trying out for sports, or was it just to tune up and tighten our glutes? How many extra sprints did we have to run around the varsity track to the point of exhaustion to achieve our goals? For us swimming enthusiasts, how many times did we almost drown before we felt proficient in the freestyle or the breaststroke? What about the hours of voice lessons and rehearsals we endured in the school and college chorus before we could perform? Commenting on how much time she devoted to practice, one of its members recalled playing on her flute the score of Swan Lake almost a thousand times before her debut which led to a standing ovation after her performance.

Practice is what we caregivers do, and it is part of the learning curve each of us masters to be proficient in our chosen profession. Do you remember how nervous you felt as a student nurse or medical student the first time you gave an injection? Do you remember how difficult it was to scale barricades or carry fire hoses during your first days of training to be a firefighter or the first time you had to pull out your gun in an arrest? How did you feel on your first run as a paramedic? Were you comfortable in being called a "rookie" the first time on the job? How did you feel as a student teacher facing thirty-five fifth graders? How many pieces of paper are crumbled and thrown on the floor in an attempt to write an essay or an article? What about the hours of intern training that most caregivers must complete for licensure or certification?

Training and internships prepare us to deepen our skills, to gain insight, and become more efficient through practice. Practice also helps us learn from our mistakes as we gain wisdom through trial and error. Because of repeated repetition of an activity, skills are learned. Such was the experience of Dale, an art therapist who was a member of an interdisciplinary team at a large rehabilitation center who learned through trial and error to become competent in his chosen profession.

Gaining Insight Through Trial and Error

Dale had achieved a certain confidence and skill as an art therapist at a large rehabilitation center. Years of developing his practice, always seeking personal improvement, helped him achieve a reputation from his team members. He was known for his impressive results with semi-depressed patients who have lost some motor functions due to a brain injury. He achieved a unique skill of being patient, even if the fires of impatience were raging within him. He credits his success with constantly reviewing his skills and giving himself time to question and evaluate his methods as a caregiver. Step by step, Dale began to understand the discipline of practice that is similar to what Dr. Atul Gawande advocates for healthcare. Dale was able to discern through trial and error the best options for treatment. He began to understand the discipline of practice. Through his use of repeated actions, he honed his skills to perfection. In this sense, practice has to do with a focus on the process of personal and professional improvement.

Another meaning of practice has to do with one's professional work or business, such as the practice of law, a physician's practice, or that of a nurse practitioner. In Dale's case, it was the practice of art therapy. Dale's work was a practice wherein each day and each encounter demanded an openness and an attitude of hospitality. The expectation and performance of skills with a spirit of selflessness, and a truthfulness that engendered trust were the skills Dale developed over time. While most of his clients struggled with the acceptance of being partially paralyzed, drifting in and out of their fears, Dale knew he had to be their moor, their anchor, where they could tether their anguish in some cases or the hopelessness they felt. Practice took on a different meaning, one that recognized the needs of the patient or client come first, even when one is having a bad hair day. Such was his experience with Bart Morgani, a sixty-something-year-old construction worker. One day on the job, he felt dizzy, and before he knew it, passed out, only to awaken in the emergency room. Upon diagnosis, it was discovered that he suffered a cerebrovascular accident, commonly called a stroke. He had a history of being overweight, smoked, and had high blood pressure.

Bart started to respond in the ambulance on the way to the hospital as if in a dream, waking up and wondering why he was in an ambulance. By the time he arrived in the emergency room with the staff continuing the protocol for stroke victims, he felt more confused. Used to doing everything himself, he tried to get up, wanting to go home, when he realized he could not move his right leg. It seemed stuck to the gurney he was lying on. He didn't realize he also was hooked up to a heart monitor and also an intravenous drip. In a daze, he looked at the nurse who began to reposition him on the gurney, as he struggled to put words to sounds as he mumbled, "What has happened to me?" Bart spent a few days in Intensive care, then went to the stroke unit where he responded well to medications and treatments. Within less than a week or so, he was transferred to a nearby rehabilitation center. Dale's first encounter with Bart came the day after he was admitted to the rehabilitation center. Bart was in a wheelchair in the center's activity room, after finishing some physical therapy. Dale introduced himself and asked if he could pull a chair over to talk with him. He wanted Bart to know that he was a member of the interdisciplinary team and asked if he could do an admitting evaluation. Bart's response was flat and monotoned. "Do what you need to do. I'm not going anywhere." Dale responded, "Mr. Morgani, may I call you Bart? I'd like to do an admitting evaluation, but I sense your frustration in not being able to go anywhere?" "Damn!" Bart interrupted, "Look at me! One day I can run circles around the guys at work, and then the next, here I am in a wheelchair. What the hell can you do for me?" Again, it was not about Dale, but about Bart, as he was attempting to adjust to his new normal.

The challenge was clear and the invitation complex. On one hand, the passive invitation to come and do what you need to do, and on the other, the active cry for help. To complicate it more, Bart didn't have a clue how art therapy could help him recover and gain confidence. He didn't know anyone on the job who did art in their spare time. He was a construction worker, a craftsman builder, rough and tough with guys who had their own lingo and culture. Dale had a flashback just before his graduation from high school, when he had to pick up his father from a construction site. He was taken back by the lingo of his father's co-workers. "Give me the mother fucking hammer Bill; Do you have all your goddamn tools?" and "Get your ass moving, Joe, it almost quitting time."

"Bart," Dale responded, "we are going to work together, to reactivate those brain cells and neurons that were damaged because of your stroke. But I need your help. There will be days like today, when you feel like, "What's the use?" There will also be days that you will feel accomplishments because of the hard work you have done. What I can guarantee you, is that working together we can achieve some goals step by step." Bart and Dale began a journey that day, one in which through the discovery and practice of art, Bart's mood began to change.

Dale learned that Bart loved to cook recipes he learned from his Italian grandmother. She told him that heaven smells like an Italian kitchen. He talked about the homegrown tomatoes he raised to make spaghetti sauce. Dale asked Bart to imagine walking through the garden. What was it like? You could see the pride he had, as his eyes glistened over how his family and dinner guests would marvel at the taste of the sauce. One evening, his cousin visiting from Rome asked about the sauce and who made it. He said it was similar to what would be served in the best restaurants in Rome. Bart swelled up like a peacock, smiled and said "Si, questa cena e molto buono, ce la farà questa mangare." ("Yes, this dinner is very good. I made it.") Dale and Bart would spend time exploring Bart's Italian heritage, especially some of the great masterpieces of Italian art. They went through a scrapbook that Bart's wife, Angelina, brought to show pictures of their recent trip to Rome. While there are many ways to stimulate the nervous system, to activate neurons and muscle, one look at Michelangelo's David or Bernini's colonnade can bring awe and amazement. "Bart," Dale asked, "Remember the first day we met and you questioned what could art therapy do for you? You are Italian, art is in your blood." Bart learned that art can help him focus, help with his dexterity, change his mood, and in some ways inspire hope for the future. Dale was persistent, always vigilant to help Bart discover new ways to stimulate his nervous system and mood. It was about practice, day in and day out, and building a trusted relationship that helped Bart dig deep into his own Soul and inspired him to continue on the road to recovery. Under the mask of this hardcore construction worker was a world of possibilities and a gentle spirit that inspired him, despite the challenges he faced. After six weeks of intensive therapy, Bart was ready to walk out of the rehab center with a few cracks and fissures in the macho mask he so desperately wore.

The Art of Practice

While one has to practice to become more skilled and efficient, practice can also be understood to mean a particular type of work, such as a medicine, dentistry, fire prevention, the law, or a counselor. One can be called a practitioner, like a general practitioner, or a nurse practitioner. Another can have a law practice, or a counseling or coaching practice. There is something dynamic in having a practice, as the practice itself, along with the practitioner, is constantly evolving. Thus, we hear one practicing the art of medicine, or being engaged in the healing arts. If we agree that practice is important to master our professional skills and we, as caregivers, may be involved in a particular practice or occupation, is it possible for us to envision and even entertain, that the art of caregiving as not only a practice, but a spiritual practice? As discussed in Chapter One, the dance of caregiving involves an interplay between the caregiver and the one receiving the care. Each is challenged during this dance, step by step to create new steps, as the tasks of caregiving lead the caregiver to a deeper understanding of healing and transformation. Similarly, the act of caregiving challenges the one receiving care to be vulnerable, receptive, and hospitable in accepting the care that is given. Each supports the other like pilgrims on a pilgrimage, a journey of self-discovery. We can speak of many different types of caregiving, and many different recipients of that care. No matter how short or extended the encounter is between the caregiver and the one being served, the opportunity for personal and professional growth exists.

I believe that caregiving is a practice and as such, has a unique art to it. This art of caregiving, while not consciously seen or experienced as such, has qualities of having a spiritual foundation. The art of caregiving may be viewed as a spiritual practice when technical skills are interwoven with compassion and care. What makes the practice of caregiving a spiritual endeavor is that the act of caregiving invites both the caregiver and the one seeking care to listen to the promptings of their Soul. Herein lies the truth of their transformation. The ordinary becomes extraordinary, the work becomes a calling, and the art of caregiving becomes a healing art.

There is a firm purpose by the caregiver to serve, a selflessness to use one's talents and skills for the care of the one seeking help. Caregivers want to build relationships with those seeking their care. We may ask, what motivates us? What sustains us in the tasks of caregiving? What is that unique life force or energy that motivates us into action? Think of the unique calling that led you to become a caregiver and the values that sustain you as a caregiver. Caregiving becomes a spiritual practice, because each participant is challenged daily to respond to those who are in need, those who suffer, those who are in danger from floods, hurricanes, earthquakes or wildfires, and those who are ill, those who are victims of domestic violence, those that need coaching and mentoring, and care to those who are elderly and dying. This is a heroic enterprise and yet, we do it day in and day out. The response is a practice. The how and why we do it is what makes caregiving a spiritual practice.

The Rituals of Practice

Each of the different caregiver professions has their own rituals for receiving new members, for belonging, and sustaining them within the profession. They have codes of conduct, codes of ethics, and procedures to follow. Remember the safety protocol of the first responders and the firefighters as retold by Allison in Chapter Four? By the time they arrived at the site, the aircraft was engulfed in flames. The possibility of the gas tanks exploding prevented them from risking their lives to save the pilot, whose cabin was already engulfed in flames. Consider the rituals you experience when you want to see your primary physician: make an appointment, check in, checking identity, insurance, and medications. There is a comparable ritual of triage screening in a busy emergency room or something as routine and yet critical, as washing one's hands before and after visiting a patient or client to prevent the spread of infection is yet another ritual we practice.

Rituals are both exciting and routine, sometimes bordering on the scale of pure drudgery. First responders check and replace the stores of emergency drugs and equipment after each run. Nurses check and recheck the "crash" cart used for code blues (a warning that someone is in need of CPR) on the hospital floors. After each fire, firefighters clean and reroll fire hoses, as well as prepare the truck for the next emergency. These rituals have helped in the development of best practices in each profession. We are familiar with the safety regulations when we fly, the protocols for first responders, or some of the different protocols and best practices in medicine. It was the ritual of going over the checklist that Captain "Scully" Sullenberger used with his crew that saved all aboard when the engines failed, and the plane landed in the Hudson River. The crew was prepared for such an emergency.

Ritual Practices in Different Spiritual Traditions

Consider the different ritual practices of the many spiritual traditions where a practice is a form of asceticism and discipline such as meditation, yoga, ritual prayers, singing or chanting. Each tradition and practice begin with a unique intention and goal by the practitioner that requires a firm purpose of character, strength of will, and determination. The dancing of the whirling dervishes of the Sufi Islamic tradition is one such spiritual practice that seeks union with the transcendent, the Holy Other, the Divine. Dancing becomes the ritual and discipline. The different practices of meditation, the reading of Sacred Scriptures from many spiritual traditions, or the repetition of a prayer or rosary beads or knotted threads in the Buddhist, Catholic, Hindu and Islamic traditions, are other examples of a spiritual practice where repetition and concentration lead one to a deeper meditative and prayerful state.

Ancient healing practices acknowledged discipline as necessary in providing treatment and healing remedies. The Hippocratic Oath and ethical codes of practice establish principles that many caregivers follow today. Caring for those in need of our care is an integral part of many spiritual and religious traditions. "The very essence of spirituality" maintains Thomas More "is to tend to physical and emotional illnesses."[131] Seeking balance and integration of body and Soul are reflected in the Chinese notion of yin and yang, symbolized by an image in which each half contains a bit of its opposite. Jewish healing practices stress being right with God, the creator and healer, as well as follow the principles of the Torah in discovering the Kabbalistic wisdom to promote health and treat disease. The Gospel mandate of

Matthew in caring for the least members of a community in the Christian tradition, are known and practiced as the corporal works of mercy.

Less Profound Rituals

Other rituals could be as simple as brushing your teeth, your morning routine or walking your dog, going to the park to run, or the gym to exercise. It could be the preferences we have for food and preparing it. We have our set routines in how we live and relate to others. Some of us like to have a lite supper. Others prefer to make dinner their main meal. Each of us has a different way of slowing down in the evening, using rituals such as reading, spending time with family, watching an old movie on TV or listening to classical music, while others crash after a stressful day. We take a favorite route on the way to work, and as caregivers, set about the work at hand as normal as it can be. Caregivers are also ready, even hypervigilant, to drop everything for an emergent situation. How many times have we heard "my day is not going the way I planned," as if we could predict the future.

Rituals engage us in life and its daily routines. Caregivers are trained to follow procedures and protocols that define, in a particular way, how we will respond to a particular situation. As such, may we introduce the word "ritual" to also explain a protocol? Are they not the same as using "ritual" as a designated way of performing a task? The outcomes, of course, are the intended goals of the intervention in meeting the needs of those served. The meeting between caregiver and the one served becomes an opportunity for healing and transformation. In the relationship that is formed, each is sustained in the act of giving and receiving. The following story of two twins, Elliot and Benjamin, relates how two semi-estranged twins came together and rediscovered the spiritual bond they have as brothers through the dance of caregiving.

"Mrs. Jones, I Think There is Someone Else Up There."

From their earliest memories, Elliot and Benjamin had a desire to support and care for each other. They were fraternal twins, who from their earliest years were encouraged to be independent and not be like other twins, at the request of their father. A paradox indeed. Each had their own group of friends, went to different high schools, one travelled to the west coast, and the other remained near home. Their arrival into the world was even more of a surprise, when six weeks before their mother's due date, the water in which they had hitherto inhabited, seemed to disappear. Elliot was the most rambunctious and arrived first. He weighed just under three pounds. All seemed to be in order, until to the amazement of their mother and everyone else in the room, the doctor pronounced incredulously: "I think there is someone else up there!" And of course, there was. Elliot's brother Benjamin, weighing just over three pounds. They used to joke that their mother never got over the surprise.

Fast track sixty-five years to Benjamin being admitted to the hospital suffering from COPD, or Chronic Obstructive Pulmonary Disease. His wife had died two years earlier and they had no children. While Elliot and Benjamin had visited with each other throughout the years, they never had the opportunity to explore with each other the different life paths they took. Elliot, who now was divorced, and living by himself, was shocked to hear Benjamin's poor prognosis. Benny, as he liked to be called, could no longer live on his own, and even before one or the other could ask for help or offer an invitation, Benny said, "I just want to go home." Of course, you do," Elliot said, "I want you to come home with me." Their embrace knocked the air out of each of them, as they knew for the first time in a long time, that their love for each other would make it easier as twins in their journey of caregiving. The doctors did not give Benny a good prognosis and told him he had six to twelve months to live. Elliot was determined that he did not want his twin brother to die alone. Before they knew it, Benny was stable enough to be discharged.

Neither brother was prepared for the tasks of caregiving nor the demands of coping with a chronic pulmonary disease diagnosis. The visiting nurse set up a program for Benny and was always a call away. Some days were better for Benny. Some days were better for Elliot. And some days were better for both of them while some days were, well let me say it, bad for each of them. The task for Benny was to trust his brother and also change a cultural attitude of being a victim, that is one who needs care, to an attitude of receptivity, welcoming the gift that is given. This rubbed against the grain, as everything within him screamed for independence. Independence and self-reliance are different than being a victim. Welcoming the gift of caregiving from another is an act of great courage. Elliot, on the other hand, struggled with his impatience and wished Benny would do more, even though he heard the diagnosis from his brother's doctor.

The task for Elliot was to deal with the tension between being Benny's twin brother and at the same time being his primary caregiver. At home, Benny needed complete care, assistance to the bathroom, shower, and dressing. While Benny had to struggle with asking for help, Elliot had to struggle with being the caregiver that Benny needed. Despite Elliot's experience as a registered nurse, who technically knew what needed to be done, the difference was the emotional attachment he had with his brother. It was just difficult to see Benny in his current condition. It was also more difficult to know that his brother's life expectancy was limited. In a way, after all these years, when the opportunity came to spend time with his twin brother, Elliot was confronted with what, at first, he thought was a missed opportunity. He decided to keep his feelings to himself and put them on a back burner, not realizing that his very intention was still being unconsciously processed.

About two weeks after Benny was discharged from the hospital, as Elliot and Benny were finishing breakfast, Benny remarked "Well these days have been quite a workout for the both of us, haven't they? Do you remember several years ago when we both went on the men's retreat?" Elliot nodded his head in agreement with a big Cheshire cat grin, "Sure do!" Benny continued "I remember the talking stick, a stick that was passed around in the circle for each person to speak. Each had to be respectful and listen to what the other person was saying with no commentary or interruptions. Elliott, can we do this now? We don't have a talking stick, but that wooden spoon over by the stove should do. I want to share a few thoughts. I want to listen to you and be as honest as I can, and I wish that you too can be as honest as you can." Elliot rose to get the wooden spoon and passed it over to Benny. "I too have been waiting for this moment, now that we are sort of settled," replied Elliot. "You have the spoon, go for it."

Benny then took a breath as deep as he could and hoped Elliot would not be embarrassed by what he was going to say. "You know Elliot, I have always been a crusty old barnacle, always holding in my feelings and keeping what I was thinking close to my chest. I don't know if I can find the right words but thank you. Thank you for taking me in and loving me as your brother." Tears began to flow in Benny's eyes as he continued. "I'm a mess, and as much as I want to do everything for myself, I can't. This just pisses me off. I have always been independent, in control, and now I can't even go to the bathroom without your help. I know yesterday when I nearly fell, I was careless, relying on getting there, instead of watching where I was going and asking for your help. Please forgive me for being such a burden. I hate being so vulnerable, every fiber of my manhood rebels against it, and yet, if I am truly going to love you, I must accept your gracious gift of caregiving. I must accept you."

Elliot spontaneously reached out his hands across the breakfast table to meet those of Benny. In the silence of the embrace, all that was felt and experienced was what they both had prayed for during the years of their separation. The squeeze of their clasped hands seemed to melt away the years and in this present moment, time stopped, and they experienced being a brother to each other.

What seemed like a moment was about five minutes, as each stared at the other with tears running down their flushed faces, tenderly holding each other's hands. Elliot then responded, "I guess I broke the rules, as I usually do, in reaching out to you. I wasn't sure if you were finished but I couldn't help myself." Benny agreed that he was finished and passed the wooden spoon over to Elliot. Arms folded, Elliot sat back in his chair and began. "I've always had difficulty in putting my feelings into words, you know me. Yet, when I heard about your diagnosis, and that you would have to sell your home and go to a nursing facility, something in me realized how much I have missed you and how much I wanted you to spend the remaining years of life with me. You know I am divorced, and my two sons live on the west coast. I know they would be thrilled to know you are here. You are their only uncle."

Elliot took a sip of water and knew what he was going to say would be difficult. "Benny, I know the visiting nurses and aids have been very helpful, but I must confess, I had no idea what caregiving was about. I had no idea how the twenty-four/seven responsibility would affect me. I cringe at the site of blood, let alone be responsible to help you the way I have been doing. I didn't know I had the strength. But I am learning, digging deep within me for those values I hold the most, and I am realizing that I would not want it any other way. Just as it is difficult for you to submit to receiving care, so is it difficult for me to be your caregiver. I am learning the danger or shadow side of being a caregiver. Our relationship can be uneven. I'm the one in charge, sort of like nurse Ratchet, and you are the one who has to listen. This is not what being a caregiver to you means to me. Don't get me wrong, caring for you is having an effect on me. I have to deal with my own shit, stuff I have been burying for years. Now it just pops up, almost laughing at me, wondering if I have the courage needed to confront these fear gremlins and shoo them off. I thought a few days ago, that I was to care for you and it was a one-way street. Somehow in the bond we are sharing this morning, I have come to believe that you are helping me be a better man."

Benny knew how difficult it was for Elliot to be as vulnerable as he was, always making a big deal that he was the older twin, damn, *just four minutes older*! As the weeks grew into months, and months into years, again at another routine debriefing as they now call it, Elliot remarked "Benny, do you remember what your doctor said three years ago, that you only have twelve to eighteen months to live? You are out doing him by a year and a half." They both chuckled. What was also true, I as their visiting nurse witnessed, was how the bond of love they shared actually had an effect on Benny's condition. His symptoms decreased to such an extent that he was able to travel to Elliot's grandson's bar mitzvah in Los Angeles. Caregiving was a chore that eventually became a spiritual practice, in the day in and day out ups and downs of caregiving that were fed by a river of unending brotherhood. Benny's struggle became moot against Elliot's desire to care even though he felt awkward and inexperienced. Caregiving for them became a journey, a pilgrimage of sorts, as the archetypal energies guided and supported them. Each in his own way found the will and the courage to discover the healer function within one another.

The experience of Elliot and Benny is an experience we, as caregivers, can identify with and recognize. Each was hesitant to be vulnerable with each other, while at the same time, there was a desire to do so. How often we, as caregivers, feel this way with our peers and team members. While not always able to articulate fully what they were experiencing, Elliott and Benny did recognize their limitations, and their journey was grounded in the archetype of the Wounded Healer. The nature of the Wounded Healer necessitates both an interplay and relationship between the caregiver and the one cared for that develops trust, commitment, and companionship.

Caregiving becomes a crucible of Soul-making where one finds depth, value, heart, and personal meaning that the ancients understood as transformative. Similarly, those who are in need of caregiving must trust their own intuitions as people: "even very sick or burdened people have remarkable spirits, including creativity, the capacity to cope with illness and mortality, and the wonderfully human drive to find one's own life's meaning, argues Thomas Moore."[131] The journey becomes one of pilgrimage, as archetypal energies guide and support. As caregivers, our particular journey can span a lifetime in which we can trace different milestones with particular events, people, and experiences. Our journey is one of personal and professional growth.

Caregiving as a Pilgrimage

I want to introduce you to another perspective of caregiving, that of pilgrimage. Pilgrimage leads one to mystery and to one's sacred path, such as what led us into the profession of caregiving and what continues to sustain us. While we understand the meaning of journey, pilgrimage leads one to Soul. We may have read Chaucer's *Canterbury Tales* in high school or are familiar with the movie and play *"The Man from La Mancha"* and are familiar with pilgrimages to sacred sites as described in literature and art, as well as in cultural mythologies throughout history. There are many sacred paths and "sacred ways" that mark the world's temples and shrines, such as those at Delphi, Delos, Jerusalem, Mecca, Santiago de Compostela and Lourdes. I consider caregiving a sacred path, a unique pilgrimage, where the caregiver and the one seeking care journey together. Their journey challenges them to be faithful to their commitment to each other that could lead them to a deeper sense of themselves, as if coming home again, as experienced by Elliott and Benny.

Why Do People Go?

Jean D. and Wallace Clift, in *The Archetype of Pilgrimage: Outer Action with Inner Meaning*, list fifteen different reasons for making a pilgrimage. Many of them are applicable to those who are caregivers and those who are in need of care, such as to draw near to something sacred within themselves, to have the opportunity to seek pardon and reconciliation, to hope when hope seems elusive, and ask for a miracle, to give thanks, to express gratitude to the Divine, to answer an inner call to go as a caregiver, to regain lost or forgotten parts of one's life, to honor a vow and to prepare for death.[132] Here lies the hypothesis of this work, that caregiving is a pilgrimage, a sacred work where, for whatever reasons we caregivers have, we come to experience the transcendent nature of the work we do and in doing so we are healed and transformed. Caregiving is a spiritual practice.

Wholeness and a renewed understanding of one's self can to be borne out of the joys and trials of caregiving. The cycle of descent, journeying and returning is completed, as wisdom gained from the experience becomes transformative. Pilgrimage is also etched in the hearts of those seeking healing, who venture mythically on the path to wholeness. Crossing a threshold is dangerous, because what is on the other side is unknown. Richard R. Niebuhr speaks of how pilgrims perpetually search for those opportunities that satisfy their inner longings. Crossing over a threshold into an experience of pilgrimage marks one, not only physically, but also soulfully. He writes: "what we apprehend outwardly becomes part of the lasting geography of our Souls; the pilgrim in us begins to awaken".[133]

The nurse, the physician, the counselor, pastor, spiritual leader, and coach, the first responder, emergency medical responder, the safety officer and firefighter, the educator and mentor know how the geography of their Souls leads them to excel as caregivers. Pilgrims mark their journeys in the soil of the sacred paths they create with their sweat, tears, and often blood. Those who are in need and their caregivers do the same in the patient long-suffering that each may experience. Life has its way of giving us our share of painful experiences as caregivers.

Thresholds are crossed during preparations, leave-taking, and new beginnings, as well as during participation in the spirituality of the pilgrimage itself. Pilgrimage evokes an act that has symbolic meaning in which each participant seeks to transform the journey into an active and dynamic event. According to Robert Johnson, pilgrimage "becomes a symbol-in-motion that carries the power of the inner world into visible and physical form".[134] As caregivers, are we aware of how the invisible world, our Soul, speaks to us? What do we long for as a caregiver? Our caregiving can be a journey and pilgrimage that has symbolic and archetypal meanings that also makes the power of the inner world visible between the caregiver and the one being served. The pilgrimage of healing according to Campbell, "is symbolical of that divine creative and redemptive image which is hidden within all of us, only waiting to be known and rendered into life."[135]

In answering an inner call to participate in such a journey, the one who is in need of caregiving, as well as the caregiver, discovers that the path they have chosen leads them to a greater understanding of each other and to personal transformation.

The journey becomes a path to where one is going, that is marked by the many, often unplanned crossings of thresholds that define it. Caregivers become the facilitators and the tour guides, assisting those embarking with them on the journey to healing. It can come as a surprise to caregivers that as tour guides, they too become pilgrims. A good tour guide facilitates the traveler's arrival to a moment of discovery and then stands back; a bad one talks too much and blots out the moment with babbling about his own discoveries. The good tour guide listens for clues to where the traveler might like to go next; the bad one has a set itinerary that is primarily designed for his own convenience.

The good tour guide is widely travelled and delights in opportunities to serve a diversity of clients; the bad one is fearful and disparaging of "foreigners." The bad tour guide becomes hysterical when plans go awry, and an unforeseen detour is required; the good one deals with this as an adventure, fodder for a great story of how the trouble was overcome, the problem understood, an insight learned, a transformation made possible.

As you have been warned many different times, the practice of caregiving is not for sissies. There are trials, rabbit holes to fall into, dangers in not caring for one's self and also experiencing the shadow sides of caregiving and running the risk of compassion fatigue and burnout. We began with the importance of practice, then explored how we, as caregivers, may have a practice. We explored the patience of Dale as an art therapist and were drawn into the story of Elliot and Benjamin. Finally, we concluded with realizing that we, as caregivers are pilgrims on life's journey. Our concluding Chapter Ten: Our Tank is Almost Empty helps us understand the symptoms and the causes of compassion fatigue and burnout. What we will discover is that because we care, because we give compassionate care, naturally, we are prone to fatigue and exhaustion. Because we care, we may be prone to compassion fatigue and her two sisters, burnout and secondary traumatic stress. These are common experiences of caregivers and not something to be considered as extraordinary. Compassion fatigue is what most caregivers experience. Building and strengthening one's compassion resilience in rediscovering those interior strengths within is what guides caregivers through the storms of caregiving.

Timeout: A Moment of Reprieve

Time for a stop on the journey. Take your time to reflect on the questions below. Again, this is not a test, no perfect scores, you are a winner just the way you are.

1. Was there a moment during this chapter when you could identify with your own journey as a caregiver?

2. Is identifying caregiving as a spiritual practice new for you? In light of the previous chapter on spirituality, can you give an example of how you were empowered as a caregiver?

3. Were the stories of Dale and Bart, Elliot and Benny compelling to you and in what ways?

Chapter 10 - Warning: Our Tank is Almost Empty

Introduction

We have within us the human capacity to push forward even when it hurts. In the midst of confusion, exhaustion, and stress, we have the reassurance that we will find the interior strength to forge ahead, find the necessary fuel, take a short reprieve, and carry on. We, as caregivers, have had many experiences of just sucking it up and continue relying (hopefully) on our reserve. A little bit of pressure here, a little bit there, always believing we can go on until we can't. Forging ahead, often not being conscious that our tank is almost empty. Sputter, sputter, until one extra shift, one more experience of a traumatic event, one more time we have to stuff our feelings, and staying with the metaphor of driving, we have to pull over on the side of the road. We had just enough left, maybe enough, to cry out for help. Our tank is almost empty.

What happens when we are unable to hear, let alone, listen to the inner promptings of our Soul trying to warn us? Why have these warning signs fallen on deaf ears? Have we neglected them for so long that we become numb? Maybe we are simply not conscious enough of the effect secondary traumatic stress, that is being a witness to traumatic events, has on us. We run out of our reserve, and for a moment we seem paralyzed, overcome with emotion, overcome with what to do, overcome with fear that no one will listen, or understand.

My natural inclination to show compassion for others led to my experience of compassion fatigue, which had the components of secondary traumatic stress and burnout. When I came to this screeching halt over twenty-five years ago, my colleagues wondered why I couldn't keep up, and they simply did not understand, which only led to a heightened sense of abandonment. On the outside, I didn't show any signs of fatigue. Interiorly, I felt emotionally hypersensitive, like a million neurons going off that needed to be corralled. At times I felt overwhelmed, at other times, emotionally flat, and still other times oversensitive, experiencing a short fuse as I was unable to defend myself.

What I was experiencing may have reminded my colleagues on an unconscious level of what they, too, may have been experiencing. I just remember how much I needed them to understand and at the same time, how much they didn't. I knew if I had been in a terrible accident or injured at work, they would understand. The image that emerged was that I was in a hospital bed with casts and my broken leg pinned and up in a sling. But the train wreck I was experiencing, the lack of support, and the lack of self-care that addresses physical, psychological, interpersonal, and spiritual needs that could have helped me cope with the stress of caregiving, was missing. I was just too busy to consider them. There were, however, faint revelations that something was wrong, as I was becoming more exhausted. Burnout is a state of fatigue or frustration brought about by devotion to a cause, or way of life, or to a particular relationship that fails to produce an expected reward.[136]

I won the trifecta, as I experienced all three of these. I certainly had a passion and devotion to a cause. I supported the mission of the non-profit I was working with, and finally, when building a relationship with my two co-facilitators, there always seemed to be two against one. I was the lone man standing and often found myself in an unhealthy triangling relationship. Recall the words of Patricia Smith quoted earlier: "In order to experience a sense of peace, well-being and belonging in our world, we must learn to integrate the following into our lives: a source of strength other than ourselves, a tradition of prayer, meditation, or worship that allows us to disengage from the everyday world, and a practice of rituals that have the power to restore calmness, serenity, continuity and hope to our lives."[137] Each of these had been factors at one time or another in my life. Somehow, I got lost.

My well was dry or using another metaphor, I was bankrupt. The symptoms, like the arms of secondary traumatic stress and burnout, produced the compassion fatigue that had ensnared me. There was, however, enough reserve left to make the decision to visit a friend, Leo, who was a pastoral counselor. I remember his compassion when he invited me to come and chat if I ever needed help a year or so ago. It is important for caregivers to respond with compassion when we experience one of our teammates reaching out for help. His compassion seared through any resistance I had in seeking help. His compassion was the reason I was drawn to choose him. From a coaching or counseling perspective, this was about building a therapeutic and trusting relationship.

Leo was most generous in making time to see me. We set up a schedule for my visits three times a week. I didn't realize how much I needed his arms of compassion to keep me falling off a cliff of despair. He introduced me to the term burnout, which was a new concept for me. After a month, I remember asking him how much longer it will take for me to get back on my feet. I had taken a leave of absence and was about to apply for the company's disability. I felt at this moment, this was going to take more time and effort than what I expected. I wanted to know more about burnout, so I asked Leo, "on a scale of one to ten, how serious do you feel my experience of burnout is?" Leo responded truthfully as I knew he would, that he felt the degree of my burnout was between eight and nine, and he considered ten irreversible.

I was numbed by his words. Even being stunned was an emotion that could not surface. He asked me how long I had been in this conflicted situation of wearing myself out. Three years, I responded. I had been working with this consultant firm hired by the non-profit for three years. Then Leo said, "It will take you three years to recover. One day you will find that you crossed over the bridge and you will know the difference. You are bankrupt and have to restore your energy, to pay off the debt. You know, burnout is a physical and emotional exhaustion that is caused by stress. This type of stress leads to disillusionment and depression."

I remember asking Leo, still hanging on to a remnant of my past behaviors, that I wanted to do what was best for me and what the Holy Spirit wants of me. I laugh now at his response. Calmly he responded, "When you feel the most conflicted or overwhelmed, do what is the easiest. I want to repeat this. It is important for you to choose what is the easiest choice when you feel overwhelmed when many choices race through your consciousness. That is what the Holy Spirit is asking of you." The words did sink in, and I attribute them to helping me recover. Imagine, do what is the easiest in a world of getting it done yesterday! That was over twenty-five years ago. So, what's in a name, when you hear compassion fatigue, burnout and secondary traumatic stress?

What's in a Name?

Before we explore the history, the research, the symptoms, and the experience of compassion fatigue and its components of burnout and secondary traumatic stress, as well as its treatment and successful outcomes, I'd like to begin with examining the words compassion and fatigue, themselves. What is in a name? Seems from the get-go, compassion fatigue is a state of exhaustion. We, as caregivers, experience vicarious trauma due to our practice of compassion in the work we do. Recall our earlier discussion of the wounded healer in Chapter Six, *Love is a Wounded Healer*. *"What's in a Name?"* Juliet asks Romeo in William Shakespeare's *Romeo and Juliet* (II, ii). A name identifies, as well as reveals a hidden meaning. Parzival, when asked his name by his cousin Signue responds in French *"Bon fiz, cher fiz, bea fiz*—that's what they used to call me, those who knew me at home." There was a hidden meaning to his name, which means 'Pierce-through-the-heart' or said another way, a person who endures suffering.[138]

The same can be said about compassion fatigue. It is all in its name, compassion good; fatigue, well, not so good. No time to admit any sign of weakness or fatigue. God forbid, that we need to take a few days off here or there. We, as caregivers, understand the demands that compassion has on us. To enter the world of the one who needs care, is to enter a world of possible suffering, unanswered questions, doubts, fears and pain. It means to suffer with them. Hence the meaning of the word compassion, Latin for with or together, *com,* and to suffer with, *passion.* This is an important point, compassion fatigue is not something extraordinary, or a mental health stigma for a designated few. Compassion fatigue occurs because caregivers care. Let me repeat this: *Compassion fatigue occurs because caregivers care!* It is an integral side effect of being a caregiver. Charles Figley begins his book about compassion fatigue with these words: "There is a cost to caring. Professionals who listen to clients' stories of fear, pain, and suffering may feel similar fears, pains, and sufferings because they care."[139] Caregivers struggle to show compassion. The question then becomes, how do caregivers deal with the fatigue and exhaustion that is normal for them? How do they prevent the extreme symptoms of fatigue and exhaustion and build up resilience? Compassion defines who we are. It is the tonic that refreshes humankind. On the other hand, we are not gods, even though we perform sacred work. We can and do run out of energy that needs to be replaced. There is an interior discipline and resilience that we must create to address the gremlins lurking about us.

The Discipline of Compassion

While most would agree that compassion is a value to be lived, its practice is often difficult in a culture that values competition and individualism. Gawande suggests that selflessness, the art of accepting responsibility for the other and placing those needs ahead of one's self, is necessary and demands an interior discipline.[140] Self-care is not being selfish but is the discipline or guardrails that channel compassion. Another word for discipline might be temperance, the ability to temper and guide one's energy in making soulful decisions. There are different expressions of compassion, multifaceted, somewhat like the different levels of hospitality discussed in Chapter Five. Three aspects of compassion focus on the caregiver and his or her response to the one in need; secondly on the interchange between the caregiver and the one seeking care, and thirdly, on the compassion that the caregiver needs to listen to the interior promptings of his or her Soul. Does the caregiver hear the cry of the one in need? Does the one in need have a story to tell and needs a compassionate ear? Finally, does the caregiver take the risk, showing compassion for his or herself in exploring what the stirrings the Soul wish to articulate?

Henri J. M. Nouwen, Donald P. McNeil, and Douglas A. Morrison argue that compassion is more than a general kindness or tenderheartedness: "Compassion asks us to go where it hurts, to enter into places of pain, to share in brokenness, fear, confusion and anguish." Listen to how these words resonate with an invitation to understand the story of the one seeking care, and most importantly, how these actions resonate within our Souls. The authors continue, "Compassion requires us to cry out with those in misery, to mourn with those who are lonely, to weep with those in tears. Compassion requires us to be weak with those who are weak, to be vulnerable with the vulnerable, powerless with those who are powerless. Compassion means full immersion in the condition of being human."[141]

Notice the compelling demand of the caregiver to reach out and understand the story of the one in need as a member of the community and thus, support community efforts in the alleviation of social issues. On the other hand, there is a subtle, almost hidden invitation, to allow one to recognize these feelings within one's self. Yes, there are times we experience loneliness. We feel the need to cry and we understand that we experience weakness and vulnerability. At times, especially when we seem to be most strong, we find ourselves the most powerless. In the condition of being human, we, as caregivers, share what all caregivers experience around the world, namely the universal practice of compassion in our work.

We care, and this is the starting point of all that we do as caregivers. No matter how objective we believe we are, we experience the trauma, the pain and suffering of those we care for, even when we struggle to remain emotionally detached. Because we care, sometimes we get exhausted, and sometimes we need help to carry the burden of emotional, physical, and psycho-spiritual experiences we carry. The cords that tie us up with the misconception that we have to do it all ourselves need to be loosened and better to be loosened by our own methods and practice. It is better to make a connection with a family member, friend, colleague, or pastoral counselor than to have these cords cut in an emergent situation. Dr. Eric Gentry suggests we have a compassion resiliency safety net when we empower one or two people who know us well and care about us. Choose those who are strong enough to withstand any deflection when we become symptomatic or when we become consistently divergent from the ways we normally act.[142] No matter where we start, no matter what our unique philosophy or spiritual tradition may be, compassion is known universally around the world. Who do you know or rather who are you drawn to because of their compassion? That is what drew me to Leo. I knew he cared.

The Universality of Compassion

Compassion is held in high regard and is ranked among the greatest by all of the major religious traditions. The practice of compassion is implied in the Golden Rule which paraphrases Matthew 7:12: "Do to others what you would have them do to you." The Oxford Centre for Interfaith Studies highlights this Golden Rule as part of the Declaration of a Global Ethic. This was formulated at the Parliament of the World's Religions held in Chicago in 1993 by Hans Küng and Karl-Josef Kuschel. Some examples from this declaration are described below.[143]

Within the Hindu tradition, a verse from the Mahabharata articulates the Golden Rule: "This is the sum of duty: do naught unto others which would cause you pain if done to you" (XIII, 114). Compassion is called *DAYA,* and along with charity and self-control, is one of the three central virtues of the Hindu Tradition.[144] In the Jewish tradition, God is the Compassionate Holy Other and is invoked as the Father of Compassion, suggests Khen Lampert. The words of Leviticus articulate how the compassion of God is lived out in daily life: "You shall love your neighbor as yourself (19:18).[145]

Foremost among God's attributes in the Muslim tradition are mercy and compassion. Each prayer and significant action is begun by invoking God the Merciful and Compassionate. The Golden Rule is articulated in An-Nawawi 40, Hadith 13 of the Islamic tradition: "No one of you is a believer until he desires for his brother that which he desires for himself."[146] Native American tradition articulates the belief that the foundation of spirituality is respect for life. The Great Law of Peace was founded by the Iroquois Nations in the late tenth century.

The democratic ideals of this charter inspired Benjamin Franklin, James Madison and other framers of the US Constitution in their writing of the constitution and the Bill of Rights.[147]

The sacred scriptures of Sikhism, the Guru Granth Sahib, contain many angs (sayings) of the 16th century Guru Arjan Dev Ji, who gives a Sikh perspective of the Golden Rule: "Do not create enmity with anyone as God is within everyone" (Singh 258). The sacred writings of Confucianism suggest: "Do not do to others what you would not want them to do to you" (Analects of Confucius 15, 25)."

Lorne Lander defines compassion in the Buddhist tradition as "recognizing that it is a state of mind or heart. Buddhism defines *compassion* as a mental state of wishing that others may be free from suffering. In the Samyutta Nikaya V, it is written: "A state which is not pleasant or enjoyable for me will not be for another; and how can I impose on another a state which is not enjoyable to me. Compassion is closely related to love, which Buddhism defines "as cherishing others, feeling a sense of closeness with and affection for them."[148] H. H. the Dalai Lama speaks of the whole purpose of religion is to facilitate love and compassion, patience, tolerance, humility, and forgiveness. Suffering is the part of being human in which one's Soul pain cries out to be heard, understood, and relieved. The call of entering into the landscape of pain for the caregiver and the one who seeks help, is not an easy task.

Compassion requires an inner discipline of heroic proportions, grounded in one's spirituality that has a universal understanding. Compassion requires us to be weak with those who are weak, to be vulnerable with the vulnerable," maintains Nouwen, and to be "powerless with those who are powerless. Compassion means full immersion in the condition of being human"[149]

When a Light Bulb Goes On

Every teacher and professor I know has at least one favorite story about a student experiencing insight as if a light bulb goes on. They witness the face of the student brighten as if the neurons in the brain light up. One can envision over their heads, a cartoon of a light bulb.

Such was the experience of Dr. Nathan Edwards, an art professor at a local community college. One rainy day, during a semester break, Nathan, as he liked to be called, was reminiscing about the past semester. He had just finished a printmaking class, had handed in his grades, and was reviewing printed copies of the projects his students had completed for the course. He thought back at the different encounters he had with each of his students coming from a variety of cultural backgrounds and different age groups.

As most teachers do, he wondered about their futures as artists, those who were struggling to find themselves, those who did well, and those who just needed an extra elective and really were not interested in art. Then he wondered about those students who not only did well in class, but who excelled in their work and had a passion for building a career as artists. Nathan knew, along with many of his colleagues, that it was necessary to have a kind and caring heart for the students he taught. He knew it was not about him, but about a student applying the material so that it makes a difference in their life.

One such student was Alexander, whose enthusiasm and motivation in class, marked his determination to become a graphic designer. After one of the classes at the beginning of the semester, Alexander asked Nathan about his own desire to become a graphic artist. They talked about the class, and the different skills that were needed, as well as the importance of finding those professors, as he continued his education, that could best mentor him. Alex then mentioned how he was inspired by this particular class and how much it impressed him. Nathan responded, "Yes, I saw your enthusiasm as I was lecturing, and I'm pleased that you understood the lesson.

Alexander shared how he wanted to be a graphic artist and was particularly interested in Nathan's understanding of and his approach to the art of printmaking. Not only were his art projects done on time, often Alex would do an extra project that continued the theme of the first one. As the semester continued, Alex would volunteer after class to help Nathan pack up supplies. On one such afternoon, remembering the words of Nathan on the importance of finding teachers that could best mentor him, Alex asked Nathan if he would be his mentor.

Teachers are generally protective of their time outside the classroom, but this time the invitation to be a mentor resonated with him. Nathan paused and asked if he could share a story before he gave his answer.

He shared with Alex how one of his art professors in college became a mentor to him and what that meant to him as a young aspiring artist. It was that professor's desire for his students to meet other nationally known artists. He planned a field trip to visit with an artist who had been a mentor to him. Nathan recalled how the class came to his professor's mentor's studio, sat on the floor and listened to the artist talk about his work and his love of art. "Somehow," Nathan continued," like a flash of lightning, I knew deeply that I wanted to be an artist. You see Alex, that is the responsibility a mentor feels, almost like a high priest in the temple of art, to welcome one into the sanctuary. That is how I feel about you, recognizing that same spark that I felt when I was your age. Yes, of course, I will be your mentor."

Nathan and Alex continued to meet weekly until the class ended. Nathan also hired Alex as a studio assistant. They established a mentor relationship that continued through the years. Whenever Alex had a question about a different art project, he often would call or visit with Nathan during his undergraduate and graduate studies. His skills developed, and he was hired by a graphic design company in New York. His work appeared on the cover of a leading magazine depicting the new airport in Hong Kong. Nathan was gratified that those hours spend with Alex had helped Alex become an accomplished artist. Proud as a peacock, Nathan invited him back to the college to speak to his students.

Nathan never doubted his decision to mentor Alex, especially since they both came from families who considered art to be a pastime and not a career. He was sensitive to this lack of encouragement which motivated him to be a mentor, which for Nathan was indeed, a great reward. If this was not reward enough, Alex invited Nathan to host an art exposition of their works together in New York. This was the gift they gave each other as that original spark, that light that went on, became the guiding motivation for a friendship that still endures. The art of being a mentor is to facilitate another to take off, to find their wings, and discover more about themselves as they pursue their path in life. The unintended reward, however, was to become peers and colleagues. Nathan reached out in compassion, remembering the compassion shown him by one of his art professors, and in doing so, he created space to understand the story of Alex as his mentor. He discovered those interior stirrings within himself. The gift of caregiving is that the one who reaches out to serve one in need, becomes the one who is transformed and healed.

Symptoms Keep Knocking at the Door

The words of the song "I hear you knocking, but you can't come in" sums up the tension and the dance of caregiving that caregivers often experience. Something in us does hear and yet, does not hear or pay attention to the faint knocking at the door of our consciousness. Maybe our knocks are on life support, or even dead to any awareness that the knocking continues. That is the responsibility of our Soul, and like it or not, the Soul is persistent in guiding us toward healing and transformation. I am reminded of the carved inscription on the lintel over the main door of Jung's house, a quote he borrowed from the Oracle at Delphi: "Vocatus atque non vocatus Deus aderit" "Summoned or not summoned, God will be present."[150] Summoned or not summoned, our Soul will guide us. What keeps us from opening the door and saying, "Come in?" What prevents us from creating the space within us to listen, to discern, and to take action? Is it the fear of what we may discover, or is there a fear of feeling vulnerable and a fear of being shamed because we are not professional enough? Is it the fear that we will be blamed, even though studies show that it is not a flaw within the individual, but rather a systemic flaw in the organization?[151] In speaking recently with a physician who is the medical director of a large neonatal intensive care unit in the Midwest, she acknowledged that admitting any type of vulnerability among her peers is considered not only a weakness, but a sign of being incompetent in her caregiving. Is it the exterior noise of our surroundings that drowns out these interior stirrings of our Soul? Do we allow busyness to be our excuse to do this inner exploration, or to face the fears that we might have to pause, to take notice so the Soul pain within us can be attended to? The task for the caregiver is to open the door and gently introduce oneself to what needs to be addressed. Easier said than done.

So, What is Fatigue?

Returning to our metaphor of "What is in a Name?" we discover that just as the definition of compassion is multifaceted, so too, is the meaning of fatigue. The easiest definition is that fatigue is extreme exhaustion after a particular activity. Each of us can remember how exhausted we felt when we moved from one house to another. After the movers leave, we sort of plop on the coach, with every muscle of our body screaming for attention. When we speak of fatigue in the context of the caregiving we do, and as hard as it is to say, we do get exhausted and fatigued by the day in and day out work of caregiving. Sometimes the fatigue is physical, and our bodies ache because of the particular demands of that day. Christina Maslach argues that the symptoms can be physical, emotional, and spiritual. "Symptoms of physical exhaustion can be somatic complaints, weight loss or weight gain, gastric intestinal distress, insomnia, and aches and pains just to name a few."[152]

Other times, we are emotionally exhausted because we are witnesses to a specific traumatic event or experience vicarious trauma because of the work that we do. Signs of emotional fatigue can be outbursts, emotional instability, anger, suicidal ideation, cynicism, irritability, racing thoughts, sarcasm, poor concentration, violent fantasies, fears and anxiety. When the symptoms of compassion fatigue start rearing their ugly heads, we may isolate ourselves and deprive ourselves of interpersonal relationships that can support us. Relationship problems, becoming isolated, troubled relationships with coworkers, and fears of relating one's experience with another are such examples of experiencing relationship fatigue. Instead of turning toward a loved one or colleague, one turns to isolation and self-medicating with drugs, alcohol, gambling, sex, and food addictions.[153]

Of equal importance, our spiritual values may be challenged. We seem to be drifting out to sea, experiencing a loss of meaning and purpose caught in a riptide where our spiritual values seem to get lost. Caregivers experience a loss of joy and happiness. They become like robots, appearing at work to do a job but with the loss of the passion they once had. We all know through our own experiences with our peers, that some members are on the precipice of falling into compassion fatigue, burnout, or secondary traumatic stress, even PTSD.

Another form of fatigue is called burnout. Maslach (1982) with Goldberg (1998) and Leiter (2003) agree that burnout can be defined "as a psychological syndrome of emotional exhaustion, depersonalization, and reduced personal accomplishment."[154] There is an uncanny similarity between Maslach and the earlier definition by Freudenberger, who identifies burnout "as a state of fatigue or frustration brought about by devotion to a cause, or way of life, or to a particular relationship that fails to produce an expected reward."[155] Gentry & Baranosky (1998) seem to capture the essence of burnout as "The chronic condition of perceived demands outweighing perceived outcomes."[156]

Where to Begin?

If compassion fatigue, with its two sisters secondary traumatic stress and burnout is a danger to caregivers, and if the very art of caregiving presupposes we will experience pain and suffering, then how do we build the needed resiliency to protect ourselves? The easiest answer is one step at a time. The first is to become aware of and not afraid of the symptoms. They are more than just believing that they will go away and that we can deal with them. The opposite is true. They will become worse and may lead to work interruption, absenteeism, and loss of productivity. How do we become comfortable in our own skin, learning to welcome, learning to become hospitable to those stirrings of the Soul, to the Soul pain that screams for attention? Currently, two of my clients are struggling with the cultural mores that they have to do everything themselves. Both are overwhelmed, both have friends willing to help, and both have an ingrained stubbornness about seeking any help. They are experiencing the dance of caregiving.

Interestingly, as I felt the compassion of Leo, so too, are each of these responding to the compassion I have for them. How do we, as caregivers, respond to those loving invitations from family, friends, and colleagues who knock gently at our door? I guess the first step is to listen to those stirrings, and if we don't hear them, can we trust a loving person to mirror them to us? This is one of the first steps that Gentry suggests in his presentation of the three skills that are effective in resolving current symptoms and to prevent future effects.[157] The first is to connect with a friend, family member, coach, counselor, or colleague for support. Simply ask them if they could listen to what is stirring and may be causing anguish in your Soul. Remind them that listening is not giving advice. If you are afraid of the reaction that the one you love or care for might have, pause for a moment, take a deep breath, and take the risk. This is a normal feeling of being vulnerable, something that may be a new experience for you. You may suggest that you don't want them to solve or fix anything. You just want them to listen, which may be new for them. Certainly, it is reasonable for you to also reach out to a coach, pastor, or counselor. Being able to articulate your inner stirrings, as best you can, is already a step on the road to recovery.

Those in pain need to break the silence and take the risk to seek help, as well as be open to those who care about you and offer to help. We always have our answer pat when we hear the greeting "Hello, how are you doing?" and then we answer "Fine," even when we really are feeling shitty that day. "Fine" allows us to share a greeting and get on our way. I love the Italian greeting and the response "Come Sta (How are you)?" One can answer "Va bene (Very well) or one can answer "Non che Male" (there is no evil or I'm feeling sort of ok or things could be worse). The greeting invites the greeter to ask more questions, and then the floodgates are open.

Secondly, as you reach out to someone, you are already entering into the realm of storytelling. How far back do you remember a story told to you? Was it at a grandparent's house, or around a campfire at a Scout camp, or was it listening to a client in need? We all have stories to tell, so it's not that we have to rack our brain for one. Most of them are on the tip of our tongues. When was the last time you felt you were listened to and that someone was really interested in what you had to say? Stories allow us to reflect, and to envision new possibilities.

Storytelling becomes a powerful means of looking at oneself from a safe and alternate perspective.

The stories throughout this work have been gleaned from personal interviews and experiences. These stories encompass experiences of grief, primary and secondary PTSD, a child's first caregiving remembrance for his pet, parents caring for a sick child and adult children caring for their parents. There were stories of relationships, sexual abuse, auto accidents, exceptional caregiving, a physician's compassion, different life transitions, a chaplain's interventions, the dance of caregiving with two twin brothers, a professor as mentor, and a nurse's compassion with a dying person. Throughout this book, after each chapter, there are reflection questions about each of the stories that were part of that chapter. It is my hope that one or two of these struck home, giving you pause to slow down and reflect. It is my hope that you can be inspired to journal, to create a story about you. There is no script in how to tell a story. I'm sure you are a pro, especially after a beer or two. No babble, just your willingness to tell your story. You just start. Someone wants to hear your story and as you relate it verbally, or in writing, what you will discover is that the story becomes a mirror reflecting back the real you.

The third skill that helps one deal with the symptoms of compassion fatigue is to create a practice of relaxation. We have the luxury of time and it is possible to develop periods and spaces in one's day, week, or month. Have you been wanting to take that cooking class or sign up with a writer's group? What about time to read that book about travelling in Europe or planning for that fishing trip you have always put off? Do you remember being invited to learn a new form of meditation by a member of your church or synagogue? Are you willing to go to that workshop on centering prayer and learn more about your spirituality? Where do you find those opportunities to discover more about yourself as a caregiver? Can you pause and reflect on who and what gives meaning to you? Do you have or want to develop a spiritual practice? How many times do you rationalize that you are too busy? Do you put off taking that walk each morning with your friends around the neighborhood or going to the local park or the gym? Do you want to join that hiking or bicycle club?

Recovery from and avoidance of the triggers and symptoms of compassion fatigue is possible. These three practices help us, as caregivers, to develop a resilience that allows us to be faithful to that original call to be a caregiver, where we find meaning and spiritual support. We can continue to have a passion for our work because in so many ways, our caregiving defines who we are. In strengthening our relationships in allowing ourselves to be vulnerable, we rediscover the value of those who support and sustain us. Each step forward is one more step where we gain self-confidence and resilience in times of stress.

Resting Places Along the Way

Like any pilgrimage, there are resting places along the way. In Chapter One, *The Dance of Caregiving*, we ask the question that each caregiver faces. Do they experience the tension between taking time to sort out their personal responses to caregiving and their need of always being vigilant to those who need their care? Time to rest, and ask, are you ready to begin this pilgrimage of self-discovery? Chapter Two, *Reclaiming Soul*, presents the caregiver with a deeper understanding of Soul as the center of one's being that discerns one's acts of caregiving. The pilgrim is confronted with the opportunity of reclaiming his or her Soul, which will be an important guide on the journey. *Once Upon a Time in the Land of Oz,* Chapter Three, asks the reader to explore how one's imagination expands what they see and experience. As one travels, the pilgrim is exposed to a panorama of nature's beauty, different sights, hills and dales, people, and cities. The question for the caregiver is, are you able to empower your imagination to enter into the realm of archetypal and mythic aspects of caregiving that leads you to experience a sense of belonging?

In Chapter Four, *Truce or Consequences,* a question is raised whether the caregiver has an understanding of the tension between the logos, the rational, and the mythos, as well as the creative sides of caregiving. Greek words that seek a unity of purpose. *The Ins and Outs of Hospitality*, Chapter Five, asks the caregiver if they are ready to assume the responsibilities and duties of being a host to the stranger, the stranger they care for, the stranger who has a story to tell, and the stranger within the caregiver that seeks a voice to be heard. Chapter Six, *Love is a Wounded Healer,* asks the caregiver to explore, as well as ask if they are comfortable with their limitations as they consider themselves wounded healers. Chapter Seven, *Cultivating the Soul's Garden*, asks the caregiver if they are familiar with the art of reflection in their lives and how reflection cultivates the garden of their soul. Chapter Eight focuses on *Spirituality: The Sinew of Human Experience* and poses the question for the caregiver, "Do they experience their work as spiritual?" Chapter Nine *Practice, Practice, Practice* asks the caregiver if they are familiar with creating one's own spiritual practice as caregivers. The Soul of Caregiving concludes with Chapter Ten, *Warning: Our Tank is Almost Empty,* which questions the caregiver if they are aware of the steps to learn compassion resilience in fighting against compassion fatigue and its two sisters, secondary traumatic distress and burnout. Because caregivers care, we do experience the initial symptoms of compassion fatigue.

In summary, the caregiver's guide is not something external to ourselves but is internal. It is not a how-to-do book, but rather a journey in discovering and reclaiming one's Soul. We explored the dilemma each caregiver experiences, the meaning of listening to one's Soul, an understanding of the mythos of our vocation, the art of being hospitable, the reality that we have limitations, the need to listen to the promptings of our Soul, the sacredness of our work, the discovery that our work is a spiritual practice, and that our acts of compassion can exhaust us. Each chapter is a stop on the road of a pilgrimage, a place to rest and ponder, where each chapter becomes a new rendezvous for the caregiver to be a pilgrim, a new oasis to explore in the landscape of one's Soul. Rest at the place where you need the most time to ponder and reflect. There is no rush. If need be, stay and join the next pilgrimage. Feel free to do so, hop on or off, as you need too. There is always another pilgrimage passing through your current rest stop. Trust your insights. You know because you know. Take the risk that will enliven you. Enjoy the journey and listen to where your Soul wishes to take you.

Timeout: A Moment of Reprieve

At your own pace, give yourself a moment of leisure to reflect on each question below.

1. Has the discussion about compassion fatigue being a normal outcome for caregivers surprised you?

2. Are you aware of any symptoms of compassion fatigue and if so, what steps can you take to help yourself?

3. Because Caregivers care and therefore are drawn into the mystery of pain and suffering, how do you maintain compassion resilience?

REFERENCES

Chapter 1

1.   Gawande, Atul. The Checklist Manifesto: How to Get Things Right. New York: Metropolitan, 2009.

2.   Kearney, Michael. *Mortally Wounded: Stories of Soul Pain, Death and Healing.* New York: Touchstone, Simon and Schuster, 1996.

3.   Hillman, James. *The Dream and the Underworld.* New York: Harper and Row,1979

4.   Jung. C. G "Psychotherapists or the Clergy." Trans. R. F. C. Hull. *The Collected Works of C. G. Jung.* Vol. 11. Princeton: Princeton UP. 1977. 341-342.

5.   Rando, Theresa. *"Grief, dying, and death."* Champaign, IL: Research Press, 1984

6.   Rando, Theresa. "How to go on living when someone you love dies." New York: Bantam Books, 1991

7.   Arrien, Angeles. "The Healing Encounter." Care for the Journey: Messages and Music for Sustaining the Heart of Healthcare. Track 2. CD-ROM. Novato, CA: Companion Arts, 2005.

8.   Campbell, Joseph. *The Hero with a Thousand Faces.* Bollinger Series XVII. New York: Pantheon, 1949.

9.   Augsburger, William. *Pastoral Counseling Across Cultures*, Philadelphia: Westminster, 1986.

Chapter 2

10.   Hillman, James. *Re-visioning Psychology.* New York: Harper Colophon, 1975.

11.   Campbell, Joseph. *Thou Art That.* Ed. Eugene Kennedy, Novato, CA: New World Library, 2001.

12. Poe, Tracy N. (1999). "The Origins of Soul Food in Black Urban Identity: Chicago, 1915-1947". *American Studies International*. XXXVII No. 1 (February): 4–17.

13. Storm, Mara. *The 7 Symbolic Foods of Passover* www.lifescript.com/food/articles/t/the_7_symbolic_foods_of_p ass over.aspx 1999

14. Merton, Thomas. *The Hidden Ground of Love: Letters*. Ed. William Shannon. New York: Farrar, Straus, Giroux, 1985.

15. Barry, John, and John Connelly. *The Practice of Spiritual Direction*. New York: Harper Collins, 1982.

16. Moore, Thomas. *Care of the Soul*. New York: Harper, 1992.

17. Hillman, James *The Dream and the Underworld*. New York: Harper and Row, 1979

18. Houston Smith. *The World Religions*. New York: HarperCollins ,1991

19. Hillman, James. *The Thought of the Heart and the Soul of the World*. Dallas: Spring, 1992.

20. Moore, Thomas. *Care of the Soul*. New York: Harper, 1992.

21. Simon and Garfunkel: *The 59th Street Bridge Song*, 1970

22. Romanyshyn, Robert. *The Ways of the Heart*. Pittsburgh, PA: Trivium, 2002.

23. Hillman, James. *Suicide and the Soul*. Zurich: Spring, 1964.

Chapter 3

24. McKean, Erin. Senior Editor. *"The Oxford American Dictionary and Thesaurus."* New York, Oxford University Press. 2003

25. Avens, Robert. *Imagination is Reality* Putnam: Spring, 1980.

26. Ulanov, Anne and Barry. *The Healing Imagination: The Meeting of Psyche and Soul.*

27. McKean, Erin. Ob. Cit.

28. A Psychological Approach to the Trinity." Trans. R. F. C. Hull. *The Collected Works of C. G. Jung.* Vol. 11. Princeton: Princeton UP, 1977. (*CW* 11: 222)

29. Pearson/Atlee/Spero-Shelley. *Introduction to Workplace StoryBranding and Narrative Intelligence.* Washington, DC. The Storybrand Group, 2009/2017. To learn more visit Carol Pearson's website: www.herowithin.com.

30. Campbell, Joseph. *A Hero with a Thousand Faces.* Bollingen Series XVII. New York: Pantheon, 1949.

31. U.S. Department of Veterans Affairs, *Understanding PTSD and PTSD Treatment Booklet. PTSD:* National Center for PTSD. Washington DC. 2016

32. Woodman, Marion. *Addiction to Perfection:* Inner City Books, Toronto, 1982

33. Pearson/Atlee/Spero-Shelley. Ob.Cit.

34. Jung, C.G. On the Relation of Analytical Psychology to Poetry." Trans. R. F. C. Hull. *The Collected Works of C. G. Jung.* Vol. 15. 127. Princeton: Princeton UP, 1981.

Chapter 4

35. Kosslyn, Stephen M. and Miller, G. Wayne. *Left Brain, Right Brain: Two Sides, Always Working Together.* Psychology Today. May 7, 2014

36. Hillman, James. *The Soul's Code.* New York: Warner Books, 1996.

37. Oglesby, Pamela. *Right Brain vs Left Brain Functions.* www.owlcation.com/socialscience, 2017

38. Musgrove, Becky. *Right Vs. Left Brain: Which Rules You?"* www.Lifescript.com, 1999

39. Mc Querrey, Lisa. *What are Good People Skills.* Chron.com, Houston, 2016

40.   International Coaching Federation. *Core Competencies.* https://coachfederation.org/credential/compentencies *2017*

41.   cf: Press Ganey Patient Satisfaction Scores http://www.pressganey.com/about/news/patient-satisfactionscores-optimizing-the-patient-and-clinician-experience

42.   International Critical Incident Stress Foundation. *The Seven Stages of formal debriefing.*

43.   California Milk Advisory Board. *Happy Cows Commercial.* Sacramento, CA Dept. Of Food and Agriculture, *2017.*

44.   Studer, Quint. *Hardwiring Excellence.* Gulf Breeze, FA. Firestarting Publishing, 2003

Chapter 5

45.   Jaucourt, Louis, chevalier de. "Hospitalité." *The Encyclopedia of Diderot & Alembert Collaborative Translation Project.* Translated by Sophie Bourgault. Ann Arbor: Michigan Publishing, University of Michigan Library, 2013.

46.   Sunil, Amitabh Kant. *Branding India: an incredible story.* Noida: Collins Business, an imprint of HarperCollins Publishers India, a joint venture with the India Today Group,2009.

47.   Mandelbaum, Allen, *The Metamorphosis of Ovid. Book VIII* 273-277. New York, Harcourt, Brace, & Company. 1993

48.   McKenzie, John L. *Dictionary of the Bible.* "Hospitality." London, Geoffrey Chapman, 1976

49.   Luke 7:36-50. *The New Oxford Annotated Bible 3rd Edition.* New York. Oxford UP, 2001

50.   Acts 14:11-12. *The New Oxford Annotated Bible 3rd Edition.* New York. Oxford UP, 2001

51.   Hebrews 13.2. *The New Oxford Annotated Bible 3rd Edition.* New York. Oxford UP, 2001

52. Augsburger, William. *Pastoral Counseling Across Cultures*, Philadelphia: Westminster, 1986.

53. Madelina, Sister M. CSJ. *Hospitality Poster.* Orange, CA. Sisters of St. Joseph of Orange, CA

54. US Department of State. *What is Active Listening.* https://www.state.gov/m/a/os/65759.htm

55. Ob. Cit Sister Madelina CSJ

56. Coogan, Michael D. Editor, *Psalm 139. The New Oxford Annotated Bible 3rd Edition.* New York. Oxford UP, 2001

57. Campbell, Joseph. *Thou Art That.* Ed. Eugene Kennedy, Novato, CA: New World Library, 2001.

58. McMahon, Norbert. *The Story of the Hospitallers of St. John of God.* Dublin. M.H. Gill & Son, 1958.

59. McKenzie, John L. *The Dictionary of the Bible. Grace.* London, Geoffrey Chapman, 1976

60. Arrien, Angeles. "The Healing Encounter." *Care for the Journey: Messages and Music for Sustaining the Heart of Healthcare.* Track 2. CD-ROM. Novato, CA: Companion Arts, 2005.

61. Puchalski, Christina. The Healing Encounter." *Care for the Journey: Messages and Music for Sustaining the Heart of Healthcare.* Track 6. CD-ROM. Companion Arts Novato, CA. 2005

Chapter 6

62. Smink, E.M. Theology of pastoral care. *Certification Papers.* Milwaukee, National Association of Catholic Chaplains, 1991

63. Augsburger, William. Ob. Cit.

64. Guggenbühl-Craig, Adolph. *Power in the Healing Professions.* NY: Spring,1971.

65. Cf. Jung, G Jung. *Memories, Dreams, Reflections, and* Freud, Sigmund. *The Interpretation of Dreams.* Trans. Joyce Crick. Oxford: Oxford UP, 1999

66. Hampel, Patricia *I Could Tell You Stories: Sojourns in the Land of Memory.* New York: W. W. Norton, 1999.

67. Slattery, Dennis, P. *The Wounded Body, Remembering the Markings of Flesh*

68. Mc Kean, Erin. Senior Editor, *The Oxford American Dictionary and Thesaurus.* New York, Oxford UP, 2003

69. Jung, Carl. "The Psychology of Transference." Trans. R. F. C. Hull. *The Collected Works of C. G. Jung.* Vol. 16. Princeton: Princeton UP, 1985.

70. Campbell, Joseph. *The Hero with a Thousand Faces.* Bollingen Series XVII. New York: Pantheon, 1949.

71. Hillman, James. *Re-visioning Psychology.* New York: Harper Colophon, 1975.

72. Morrison, Toni. Memory, Creation, and Writing." *Anatomy of Memory.* Ed. James McConkey. New York: Oxford UP 1996.

73. Downing, Christine. *Only the Wounded Healer Heals: The Testimony of Greek Mythology."* Soundings 73.4 (1990).

74. Ibid. Campbell Joseph

75. Groesbeck, C. J. "The Archetypal Image of the Wounded Healer." *Journal of Analytical Psychology*, 20 (1975): 122-145.

76. Matthews, Thomas F. *The Clash of the Gods: A Reinterpretation of Early Christian Art.* Princeton: Princeton UP, 1993.

77. Kerényi, Carl. *Asklepios*: *Archetypal Image of the Physician' Existence.* Ed. Ralph Manheim. Bollingen Series LXV. Vol. 3. Princeton: Princeton UP, 1981

78. Nouwen, Henri, J. M. *The Wounded Healer.* NY: Doubleday, 1993.

79. von Eschenbach, Wolfram. *Parzival.* London, Penguin Books, 1980.

80. Chevalier, Jean, and Alain Gheerbrant, *The Penguin Book of Symbols.* Trans. John Buchanan-Brown. London: Pantheon, 1996.

81. Hillman, James. *The Thought of the Heart and the Soul of the World.* Dallas: Spring, 1992.

82. Ibid. Hillman, James.

83. Campbell, Joseph. *The Hero with a Thousand Faces.* Bollingen Series XVII. New York: Pantheon, 1949.

84. *The Masks of God: Creative Mythology.* New York: Penguin, 1968.

85. De Castro, Francisco. *"The First Biography of St. John of God."* Trans. Benedict O'Grady. Dublin: Secretariat for the English Language Provinces of the Order,1986.

86. Doniger O'Flaherty, Wendy. "Inside and Outside the Mouth of God: The Boundary between Myth and Reality." *Daedalus* (Spring, 2008):

87. Jung, Carl. *Memories, Dreams, Reflections.* NY: Vintage 1989

88. Sperry, Len. "Holistic Treatment of the Wounded Healer: Medical, Psychological, and Pastoral Aspects." *Individual Psychology* 43.4 (1987): 538-541.

89. Daneault, Serge. 'The Wounded Healer: Can This Idea Be of Use to Family Physicians?" *Canadian Family Physician.* 54.9 (2008): 1218-1219.

90. Daneault, Ibid

91. Downing, Christine. Only the Wounded Healer Heals: The Testimony of Greek Mythology." *Soundings* 73.4 (1990): 551-573.

Chapter 7

92. Bridges, William. *Transitions: Making Sense of Life's Changes.* Cambridge, Da Capo Press, 2004

93. Ob.Cit

94. *Children of a Lesser God.* Paramount Pictures, 1986

95. Merton, Thomas. *The Hidden Ground of Love: Letters.* Ed. William Shannon. New York: Farrar, Straus, Giroux, 1985. *Letter 438 and 621*

96. Ulanov, Ann, and Barry Ulanov. *The Healing Imagination: The Meaning of Psyche and Soul.* Winnipeg: Daimon, 1999.

97. Coogan, Michael D. General Editor. *The New Oxford Annotated Bible.* Third Edition. Luke 13,6-9. Oxford, Oxford UP, 2001. "A man had a fig tree planted in his vineyard, and he came looking for some fruit on it and found none. So, he said to the gardener, 'See here! For three years I have come looking for fruit on this fig tree, still I fine none. Cut it down! Why should it be wasting the soil?' He replied, 'Sir, let it alone for one more year until I dig around it and put manure on it. If it bears fruit next year, well and good; but if not, you can cut it down.'"

98. Harding, M. Ester. *Psychic Energy: Its Source and Transformation.* Princeton: Bollingen Series X, Princeton UP, 1973.

99. Bosnak, Robert. *Embodiment: Creative Imagination in Medicine, Art, and Travel* London: Routledge, 2008.

100. Poole Heller, Diane *Crash Course.* Berkeley, North Atlantic Books, 2001.

101. Ob.Cit.

102. Campbell, Joseph. *The Flight of the Wild Gander.* Novato, CA: New World Library, 2004.

103. Nuland, S.B. *How we die.* New York: Alfred A. Knopf. 1944

Chapter 8

104. Smith, Houston. *The Illustrated World's Religions: A Guide to Our Wisdom Traditions.* San Francisco, Harper, 1994.

105. Egendorf, A. *Hearing people through their pain.* Journal of Traumatic Stress, 8 (1), 1995

106. May, Rollo. *Care of Mind/Care of Spirit.* San Francisco: Harper and Row, 1982.

107. Campbell, Joseph. *Thou Art That.* Ed. Eugene Kennedy, Novato, CA: New World Library, 2001.

108. Campbell, Joseph, Ob. Cit.

109. Corbett, Lionel. *The Religious Function of the Psyche.* London: Routledge, 1996.

110. Bettelheim, Bruno. *Freud and Man's Soul.* New York: Vintage, 1986.

111. Jung, C.G. *The Psychology of Transference.* Trans. R. F. C. Hull. *The Collected Works of C. G. Jung.* Vol. 16. Princeton: Princeton UP, 1985. 230, 231.

112. Grant, Robert, *The Way of the Wound, A Spirituality of Trauma and Transformation.* Burlingame, CA: Robert Grant, 1997.

113. Pearson/Atlee/Spero-Shelley *Story Type Profiling.* Washington: Story Branding Group, 2009

114. Cf: Robert K. Greenleaf, *Servant Leadership.* New York: Paulist Press, 1977.

115. Pearson et al. Ob.Cit.

116. The Balm of Gilead is interpreted as a spiritual medicine that is able to heal Israel (and sinners in general). In *The Old Testament*, the balm of Gilead is taken most directly from Jeremiah, Chapter 8 v. 22:

117. Smith, Patricia. *To Weep for the Stranger: Compassion Fatigue in Caregiving.* Scotts Valley, CA: Create Space, 2009.

118. Berry, Thomas. *The Dream of the Earth.* San Francisco: Sierra, 1988.

119. Campbell, Joseph. *Transformations of Myth through Time.* Vol. 1, Tape 5. Tape Cassette High Bridge Productions, 1990.

120. Sing, K.V. *Hindu Rites and Rituals: Origins and Meanings.* N.Y. Penguin Books, 2015

121. Ibid. *The Inner Reaches of Outer Space: Metaphor as Myth and Religion.* Novato, CA: New World Library, 2002.

122. Paden, William, E. *Interpreting the Sacred: Ways of Viewing Religion.* Boston: Beacon, 1992.

123. Jung, C.G. *Memories, Dreams, Reflections.* New York: Vintage, 1989.

124. Grant, Robert, *The Way of the Wound: A Spirituality of Trauma and Transformation.* Burlingame, CA: Robert Grant, 1997.

125. Jung, C.G. "*Mysterium Coniunctionis.*" Trans. R. F. C. Hull. The Collected Works of C. G. Jung. Vol. 20. Princeton: Princeton UP, 1977. 330.

126. Hillman, James. *Re-visioning Psychology.* New York: Harper Colophon, 1975.

127. Mogenson, Greg. *A Most Accursed Religion, When Trauma becomes a God.* Zurich: Spring, 2005.

128. Ob.Cit - Mogenson, Greg

129. Association of American Medical Colleges. Medical School Objective Project. *Report III, Contemporary Issues in Medicine: Communication in Medicine.* Washington, DC. October,

130. Ob.Cit. - Association of American Medical Colleges

Chapter 9

131. Moore, Thomas. "The Soul of Medicine," *Spirituality and Health* 9.3 (2006): 10-11.

132. Clift, Jean Dalby, and Wallace B. Clift, *The Archetype of Pilgrimage: Outer Action with Inner Meaning.* New York: Paulist, 1996.

133. Niebuhr, Richard R. "Pilgrims and Pioneers," *Parabola* 9.3 (Fall 1984): 6-13.

134. Johnson, Robert A. *Inner Work.* San Francisco: Harper & Row, 1986

135. Joseph Campbell. *The Hero with a Thousand Faces.* Bollingen Series XVII. New York: Pantheon, 1949.

Chapter 10

136. Maslach, Christina. *Burnout: The Cost of Caring.* San Francisco, Jossey-Ross,1982.

137. Smith, Patricia. *To Weep for the Stranger: Compassion Fatigue in Caregiving.* Scotts Valley, CA: Create Space, 2009.

138. Cf. Story of Parzival, Chapter 5 Parzival as a Wounded Healer.

139. Figley, Charles. *Compassion Fatigue.* N.Y. Routledge,1995.

140. Gawande, Atul. *The Checklist Manifesto: How to Get Things Right.* New York: Metropolitan, 2009.

141. Nouwen, Henri, J. M., Donald P. McNeil, and Douglas A. Morrison. *Compassion A Reflection on the Christian Life.* London: Darton, Longman, Todd, 2008

142. Gentry, J. Eric. International Association of Trauma Professional, Certified Compassion Fatigue Professional. January 2018

143. Hans Küng, *Global Responsibility. In Search of a New World Ethic,* London/Continuum, New York SCM Press,1991

144. Bakker, Freek L. *Comparing the Golden Rule in Hindu and Christian Religious Texts.* Studies in Religion/Sciences Religieuses 2012 42:1, 38-58

145. Lampert, Khen. *Traditions of Compassion: From Religious Duty to Social Activism.* NY: Macmillan, 2006.

146. Elias, Abu Amina. *The Golden Rule and Islam.* Islam. Ru. 2013

147. Schaaf. Gregory. *American Indian Law Review.* " From the Great Law of Peace to the Constitution of the United States: A Revision of America's Democratic Roots." Vol. 14, No. 2 (1988/1989), UP of Oklahoma College of Law

148. Lander, Lorne. *The Lost Art of Compassion.* New York: HarperCollins, 2004.

149. Nouwen, Henri, J. M. *The Wounded Healer.* NY: Doubleday,1993.

150. Jung.C. G. *Memories, Dreams, Reflections.* New York: Vintage, 1989.

151. Maslach, Christina & Leiter, Michael, *The Truth About Burnout: How Organizations Cause Personal Stress and What to do about it.* San Francisco. Jessey-Boss, 1997

152. Maslach, Christina. *Burnout the Cost of Caring.* Ob.Cit.

153. Gentry, Ob. Cit

154. Maslach, Ob.Cit.

155. Freudenberger, Herbert J, and Geraldine Richelson. Burnout: *The High Cost of High Achievement.* Garden City, N.Y: Anchor Press, 1980.

156. Gentry, Ob. Cit.

157. Gentry, Ob. Cit.

About the Author

Dr. Edward M. Smink, Ph.D. has over forty years of experience in healthcare as nurse, crisis and pastoral counselor, executive leader, facilitator of mission, ethics, value and leadership formation and community health. He served on local, regional and international committees of value formation in the United States, Australia, Korea, England, Spain and Italy. His career of coaching has the foundation of his many years in different leadership positions where his skills of active listening, the promotion of ethical and professional guidelines, crisis intervention, facilitation of personal and professional goals, growth strategies, and sensitivity for and the promotion of cultural and spiritual diversity has taught him much wisdom.

Edward likes to claim that along with his academic credentials, he has learned most from his experience with colleagues who care for others and from those who needed his services. Edward's focus on coaching includes an emphasis on the development of strengths and the integration of values in personal and professional practice. He is passionate about the universal values and archetypes that unite humankind and with his background in mythological studies, enjoys discovering the unique personal stories of each client that contribute to successful outcomes. More information about Dr. Edward M. Smink can be found on his website:

www.soulofthewoundedhealer.com

11932189R00125

Made in the USA
Monee, IL
19 September 2019